Macmillan McGraw-Hill

California Standards Review Series

Mastering the California Mathematics Standards

Grade 4

Macmillan
McGraw-Hill

The McGraw·Hill Companies

 **Macmillan McGraw-Hill**

Send all inquiries to:
Macmillan/McGraw-Hill
8787 Orion Place
Columbus, OH 43240-4027

ISBN: 978-0-02-106356-7
MHID: 0-02-106356-7

Mastering the California Mathematics Standards, Grade 4

Printed in the United States of America

9 10 HES 15 14 13 12 11 10

Contents

California Mathematics Standards, Grade 4

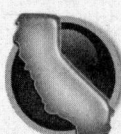

 = key standard

Number Sense

1.0 **Students understand the place value of whole numbers and decimals to two decimal places and how whole numbers and decimals relate to simple fractions. Students use the concepts of negative numbers:**

1.1 Read and write whole numbers in the millions.

1.2 Order and compare whole numbers and decimals to two decimal places.

1.3 Round whole numbers through the millions to the nearest ten, hundred, thousand, ten thousand, or hundred thousand.

1.4 Decide when a rounded solution is called for and explain why such a solution may be appropriate. *Not assessable in multiple-choice format on the Grade 4 CST.*

1.5 Explain different interpretations of fractions, for example, parts of a whole, parts of a set, and division of whole numbers by whole numbers; explain equivalents of fractions (see Standard 4.0).

1.6 Write tenths and hundredths in decimal and fraction notations and know the fraction and decimal equivalents for halves and fourths (e.g., $\frac{1}{2} = 0.5$ or $.50; \frac{7}{4} = 1\frac{3}{4} = 1.75$).

1.7 Write the fraction represented by a drawing of parts of a figure; represent a given fraction by using drawings; and relate a fraction to a simple decimal on a number line.

1.8 Use concepts of negative numbers (e.g., on a number line, in counting, in temperature, in "owing").

1.9 Identify on a number line the relative position of positive fractions, positive mixed numbers, and positive decimals to two decimal places.

2.0 **Students extend their use and understanding of whole numbers to the addition and subtraction of simple decimals:**

2.1 Estimate and compute the sum or difference of whole numbers and positive decimals to two places.

2.2 Round two-place decimals to one decimal or the nearest whole number and judge the reasonableness of the rounded answer.

3.0 **Students solve problems involving addition, subtraction, multiplication, and division of whole numbers and understand the relationships among the operations:**

3.1 Demonstrate an understanding of, and the ability to use, standard algorithms for the addition and subtraction of multidigit numbers.

 # California Mathematics Standards, Grade 4

 = key standard

Number Sense (continued)

3.2 Demonstrate an understanding of, and the ability to use, standard algorithms for multiplying a multidigit number by a two-digit number and for dividing a multidigit number by a one-digit number; use relationships between them to simplify computations and to check results.

3.3 Solve problems involving multiplication of multidigit numbers by two-digit numbers.

3.4 Solve problems involving division of multidigit numbers by one-digit numbers.

4.0 Students know how to factor small whole numbers:

4.1 Understand that many whole numbers break down in different ways (e.g., $12 = 4 \times 3 = 2 \times 6 = 2 \times 2 \times 3$).

4.2 Know that numbers such as 2, 3, 5, 7, and 11 do not have any factors except 1 and themselves and that such numbers are called prime numbers.

Algebra and Functions

1.0 Students use and interpret variables, mathematical symbols, and properties to write and simplify expressions and sentences:

1.1 Use letters, boxes, or other symbols to stand for any number in simple expressions or equations (e.g., demonstrate an understanding and the use of the concept of a variable).

1.2 Interpret and evaluate mathematical expressions that now use parentheses.

1.3 Use parentheses to indicate which operation to perform first when writing expressions containing more than two terms and different operations.

1.4 Use and interpret formulas (e.g., area = length $\times$ width or $A = lw$) to answer questions about quantities and their relationships.

1.5 Understand that an equation such as $y = 3x + 5$ is a prescription for determining a second number when a first number is given.

2.0 Students know how to manipulate equations:

2.1 Know and understand that equals added to equals are equal.

2.2 Know and understand that equals multiplied by equals are equal.

California Mathematics Standards, Grade 4

 = key standard

Measurement and Geometry

1.0 Students understand perimeter and area:

1.1 Measure the area of rectangular shapes by using appropriate units, such as square centimeter (cm^2), square meter (m^2), square kilometer (km^2), square inch (in^2), square yard (yd^2), or square mile (mi^2).

1.2 Recognize that rectangles that have the same area can have different perimeters

1.3 Understand that rectangles that have the same perimeter can have different areas.

1.4 Understand and use formulas to solve problems involving perimeters and areas of rectangles and squares. Use those formulas to find the areas of more complex figures by dividing the figures into basic shapes.

2.0 Students use two-dimensional coordinate grids to represent points and graph lines and simple figures:

2.1 Draw the points corresponding to linear relationships on graph paper (e.g., draw 10 points on the graph of the equation $y = 3x$ and connect them by using a straight line).

2.2 Understand that the length of a horizontal line segment equals the difference of the x- coordinates.

2.3 Understand that the length of a vertical line segment equals the difference of the y- coordinates.

3.0 Students demonstrate an understanding of plane and solid geometric objects and use this knowledge to show relationships and solve problems:

3.1 Identify lines that are parallel and perpendicular.

3.2 Identify the radius and diameter of a circle.

3.3 Identify congruent figures.

3.4 Identify figures that have bilateral and rotational symmetry.

3.5 Know the definitions of a right angle, an acute angle, and an obtuse angle. Understand that $90°$, $180°$, $270°$, and $360°$ are associated, respectively, with $\frac{1}{4}$, $\frac{1}{2}$, $\frac{3}{4}$, and full turns.

3.6 Visualize, describe, and make models of geometric solids (e.g., prisms, pyramids) in terms of the number and shape of faces, edges, and vertices; interpret two-dimensional representations of three-dimensional objects; and draw patterns (of faces) for a solid that, when cut and folded, will make a model of the solid.

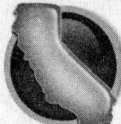

California Mathematics Standards, Grade 4

 = key standard

Measurement and Geometry (continued)

3.7 Know the definitions of different triangles (e.g., equilateral, isosceles, scalene) and identify their attributes.

3.8 Know the definition of different quadrilaterals (e.g., rhombus, square, rectangle, parallelogram, trapezoid).

Statistics, Data Analysis, and Probability

1.0 Students organize, represent, and interpret numerical and categorical data and clearly communicate their findings:

1.1 Formulate survey questions; systematically collect and represent data on a number line; and coordinate graphs, tables, and charts.

1.2 Identify the mode(s) for sets of categorical data and the mode(s), median, and any apparent outliers for numerical data sets.

1.3 Interpret one-and two-variable data graphs to answer questions about a situation.

2.0 Students make predictions for simple probability situations:

2.1 Represent all possible outcomes for a simple probability situation in an organized way (e.g., tables, grids, tree diagrams).

2.2 Express outcomes of experimental probability situations verbally and numerically (e.g., 3 out of 4; $\frac{3}{4}$).

Mathematical Reasoning

1.0 Students make decisions about how to approach problems:

1.1 Analyze problems by identifying relationships, distinguishing relevant from irrelevant information, sequencing and prioritizing information, and observing patterns.

1.2 Determine when and how to break a problem into simpler parts.

2.0 Students use strategies, skills, and concepts in finding solutions:

2.1 Use estimation to verify the reasonableness of calculated results.

2.2 Apply strategies and results from simpler problems to more complex problems.

2.3 Use a variety of methods, such as words, numbers, symbols, charts, graphs, tables, diagrams, and models, to explain mathematical reasoning.

 # California Mathematics Standards, Grade 4

 = key standard

Mathematical Reasoning (continued)

2.4   Express the solution clearly and logically by using the appropriate mathematical notation and terms and clear language; support solutions with evidence in both verbal and symbolic work.

2.5   Indicate the relative advantages of exact and approximate solutions to problems and give answers to a specified degree of accuracy.

2.6   Make precise calculations and check the validity of the results from the context of the problem.

3.0   Students move beyond a particular problem by generalizing to other situations:

3.1   Evaluate the reasonableness of the solution in the context of the original situation.

3.2   Note the method of deriving the solution and demonstrate a conceptual understanding of the derivation by solving similar problems.

3.3   Develop generalizations of the results obtained and apply them in other circumstances.

All Mathematical Reasoning standards are embedded in the questions on the Grade 4 CST.

Name _____ Date _____

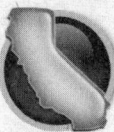

Diagnostic Test
Student Recording Sheet

Color in the bubble for each question that you answered correctly on the Diagnostic Test. For each question you did not answer correctly, your teacher may ask you to do the exercises on the practice sheet prescribed.

Question	Standard Assessed	Practice Page
○ 1	4NS1.1	A19-20
○ 2	4NS1.6	A23
○ 3	4NS1.2	A21
○ 4	4MG3.6	A61
○ 5	4NS1.2	A21
○ 6	4NS1.3	A22
○ 7	4NS1.8	A25-26
○ 8	4NS1.1	A19-20
○ 9	4NS1.8	A25-26
○ 10	4NS1.4	A35-36
○ 11	4NS3.1	A31-32
○ 12	4MG3.5	A60
○ 13	4NS1.5	A23
○ 14	4NS1.6	A23
○ 15	4NS1.6	A23
○ 16	4NS1.5	A23
○ 17	4MG1.1	A51
○ 18	4NS2.1	A29
○ 19	4NS2.1	A29
○ 20	4NS3.2	A31-32
○ 21	4NS1.3	A22
○ 22	4AF2.1	A47
○ 23	4MG2.1	A54
○ 24	4SDAP1.2	A65
○ 25	4NS3.1	A31-32

Question	Standard Assessed	Practice Page
○ 26	4NS1.9	A27-28
○ 27	4NS1.9	A27-28
○ 28	4NS3.1	A31-32
○ 29	4MG1.2	A52
○ 30	4AF1.1	A40
○ 31	4NS3.3	A35-36
○ 32	4MG3.1	A57
○ 33	4NS3.2	A33-34
○ 34	4NS3.3	A35-36
○ 35	4NS4.2	A39
○ 36	4AF1.2	A41-42
○ 37	4NS4.2	A39
○ 38	4NS1.7	A24
○ 39	4MG2.2	A55
○ 40	4NS4.1	A39
○ 41	4NS3.4	A37-38
○ 42	4NS1.9	A27-28
○ 43	4NS2.2	A30
○ 44	4AF1.2	A41-42
○ 45	4NS3.2	A33-34
○ 46	4NS3.3	A35-36
○ 47	4AF1.1	A40
○ 48	4AF1.3	A43-44
○ 49	4NS3.4	A37-38
○ 50	4AF1.4	A45

continued on next page ⟶

Diagnostic Test
Student Recording Sheet (continued)

Question	Standard Assessed	Practice Page
○ 51	4AF1.1	A40
○ 52	4AF1.5	A46
○ 53	4AF1.4	A45
○ 54	4AF2.2	A49-50
○ 55	4MG1.4	A53
○ 56	4MG3.7	A62
○ 57	4AF1.5	A46
○ 58	4MG3.5	A60
○ 59	4MG1.3	A52
○ 60	4AF2.2	A49-50
○ 61	4AF1.1	A40
○ 62	4MG3.8	A63
○ 63	4MG2.3	A56

Question	Standard Assessed	Practice Page
○ 64	4MG3.2	A58
○ 65	4MG1.4	A53
○ 66	4SDAP1.3	A66
○ 67	4SDAP2.1	A67
○ 68	4SDAP2.2	A68
○ 69	4MG3.4	A59
○ 70	4AF2.1	A47-48
○ 71	4SDAP2.2	A68
○ 72	4MG2.3	A56
○ 73	4MG3.3	A59
○ 74	4SDAP1.2	A65
○ 75	4SDAP1.3	A66
○ 76	4SDAP1.1	A64

Total Number of Questions Correct

Count how many questions you answered correctly.
Find your score in the table below and circle your level.

Far Below	Below Basic	Basic	Proficient	Advanced
0-19	20-41	42-53	54-65	66-75

Name _____   Date _____

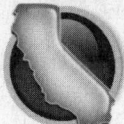

Diagnostic Test
Student Answer Sheet

Record your answers by coloring in the appropriate bubble for the best answer to each question.

1 Ⓐ Ⓑ Ⓒ Ⓓ	27 Ⓐ Ⓑ Ⓒ Ⓓ	53 Ⓐ Ⓑ Ⓒ Ⓓ
2 Ⓕ Ⓖ Ⓗ Ⓙ	28 Ⓕ Ⓖ Ⓗ Ⓙ	54 Ⓕ Ⓖ Ⓗ Ⓙ
3 Ⓐ Ⓑ Ⓒ Ⓓ	29 Ⓐ Ⓑ Ⓒ Ⓓ	55 Ⓐ Ⓑ Ⓒ Ⓓ
4 Ⓕ Ⓖ Ⓗ Ⓙ	30 Ⓕ Ⓖ Ⓗ Ⓙ	56 Ⓕ Ⓖ Ⓗ Ⓙ
5 Ⓐ Ⓑ Ⓒ Ⓓ	31 Ⓐ Ⓑ Ⓒ Ⓓ	57 Ⓐ Ⓑ Ⓒ Ⓓ
6 Ⓕ Ⓖ Ⓗ Ⓙ	32 Ⓕ Ⓖ Ⓗ Ⓙ	58 Ⓕ Ⓖ Ⓗ Ⓙ
7 Ⓐ Ⓑ Ⓒ Ⓓ	33 Ⓐ Ⓑ Ⓒ Ⓓ	59 Ⓐ Ⓑ Ⓒ Ⓓ
8 Ⓕ Ⓖ Ⓗ Ⓙ	34 Ⓕ Ⓖ Ⓗ Ⓙ	60 Ⓕ Ⓖ Ⓗ Ⓙ
9 Ⓐ Ⓑ Ⓒ Ⓓ	35 Ⓐ Ⓑ Ⓒ Ⓓ	61 Ⓐ Ⓑ Ⓒ Ⓓ
10 Ⓕ Ⓖ Ⓗ Ⓙ	36 Ⓕ Ⓖ Ⓗ Ⓙ	62 Ⓕ Ⓖ Ⓗ Ⓙ
11 Ⓐ Ⓑ Ⓒ Ⓓ	37 Ⓐ Ⓑ Ⓒ Ⓓ	63 Ⓐ Ⓑ Ⓒ Ⓓ
12 Ⓕ Ⓖ Ⓗ Ⓙ	38 Ⓕ Ⓖ Ⓗ Ⓙ	64 Ⓕ Ⓖ Ⓗ Ⓙ
13 Ⓐ Ⓑ Ⓒ Ⓓ	39 Ⓐ Ⓑ Ⓒ Ⓓ	65 Ⓐ Ⓑ Ⓒ Ⓓ
14 Ⓕ Ⓖ Ⓗ Ⓙ	40 Ⓕ Ⓖ Ⓗ Ⓙ	66 Ⓕ Ⓖ Ⓗ Ⓙ
15 Ⓐ Ⓑ Ⓒ Ⓓ	41 Ⓐ Ⓑ Ⓒ Ⓓ	67 Ⓐ Ⓑ Ⓒ Ⓓ
16 Ⓕ Ⓖ Ⓗ Ⓙ	42 Ⓕ Ⓖ Ⓗ Ⓙ	68 Ⓕ Ⓖ Ⓗ Ⓙ
17 Ⓐ Ⓑ Ⓒ Ⓓ	43 Ⓐ Ⓑ Ⓒ Ⓓ	69 Ⓐ Ⓑ Ⓒ Ⓓ
18 Ⓕ Ⓖ Ⓗ Ⓙ	44 Ⓕ Ⓖ Ⓗ Ⓙ	70 Ⓕ Ⓖ Ⓗ Ⓙ
19 Ⓐ Ⓑ Ⓒ Ⓓ	45 Ⓐ Ⓑ Ⓒ Ⓓ	71 Ⓐ Ⓑ Ⓒ Ⓓ
20 Ⓕ Ⓖ Ⓗ Ⓙ	46 Ⓕ Ⓖ Ⓗ Ⓙ	72 Ⓕ Ⓖ Ⓗ Ⓙ
21 Ⓐ Ⓑ Ⓒ Ⓓ	47 Ⓐ Ⓑ Ⓒ Ⓓ	73 Ⓐ Ⓑ Ⓒ Ⓓ
22 Ⓕ Ⓖ Ⓗ Ⓙ	48 Ⓕ Ⓖ Ⓗ Ⓙ	74 Ⓕ Ⓖ Ⓗ Ⓙ
23 Ⓐ Ⓑ Ⓒ Ⓓ	49 Ⓐ Ⓑ Ⓒ Ⓓ	75 Ⓐ Ⓑ Ⓒ Ⓓ
24 Ⓕ Ⓖ Ⓗ Ⓙ	50 Ⓕ Ⓖ Ⓗ Ⓙ	76 Ⓕ Ⓖ Ⓗ Ⓙ
25 Ⓐ Ⓑ Ⓒ Ⓓ	51 Ⓐ Ⓑ Ⓒ Ⓓ	
26 Ⓕ Ⓖ Ⓗ Ⓙ	52 Ⓕ Ⓖ Ⓗ Ⓙ	

Diagnostic Test

1 In 2005, the population of Los Angeles was about three million, eight hundred forty thousand. What is this number in standard form?

A 384,000
B 3,800,040
C 3,800,400
D 3,840,000

2 Which fraction means the same as 0.05?

F $\dfrac{5}{1000}$

G $\dfrac{5}{100}$

H $\dfrac{5}{10}$

J $\dfrac{5}{1}$

3 Which of the following are in order from least to greatest?

A 0.7, 4.5, 0.82, 1.03
B 0.7, 0.82, 1.03, 4.5
C 4.5, 1.03, 0.82, 0.7
D 0.82, 1.03, 4.5, 0.7

4 Which figure can be formed when you fold this pattern on the dotted lines without overlapping?

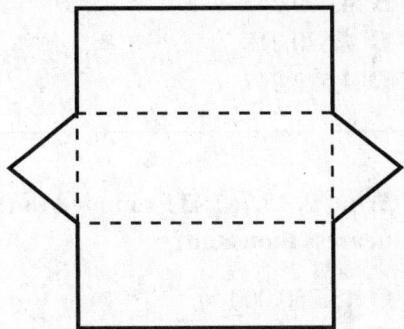

F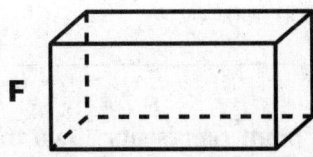

G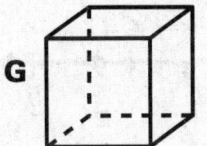

H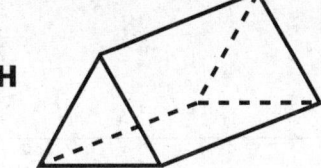

J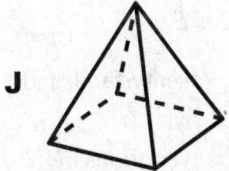

Name _____   Date _____

 # Diagnostic Test (continued)

5 Which of the following has the greatest value?

A 4,708,100
B 4,009,245
C 4,670,218
D 4,512,247

6 What is 13,762,411 rounded to the nearest thousand?

F 13,760,000
G 13,762,000
H 13,800,000
J 14,000,000

7 Which point represents $^-2$ on the number line below?

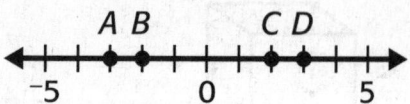

A *A*
B *B*
C *C*
D *D*

8 Which of these is the number 670,205?

F six million, seventy thousand, two hundred five
G six million, seven thousand, two hundred five
H six hundred seventy thousand, two hundred five
J six hundred seven thousand, two hundred five

9 The table shows the low temperatures in a city over four days. The temperature decreased by the same amount each day. If the pattern continues, what will the temperatures be for Friday, Saturday, and Sunday?

Day	Temp
Mon	20°F
Tue	15°F
Wed	10°F
Thu	5°F
Fri	?
Sat	?
Sun	?

A 0°F, $^-5$°F, $^-6$°F
B 0°F, $^-5$°F, $^-10$°F
C 0°F, 5°F, 10°F
D 0°F, $^-1$°F, $^-5$°F

10 Three friends shared lunch. The bill was $58. If they divide the bill evenly, about how much will each friend owe?

F $10   H $30
G $20   J $60

11
8,157
− 1,734

A 6,423   C 7,623
B 7,423   D 9,891

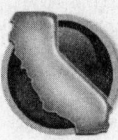

Diagnostic Test (continued)

12 Jake drew this figure.

Megan rotated the figure 90° clockwise and then traced it. Which figure below shows Megan's drawing?

F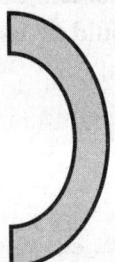

G

H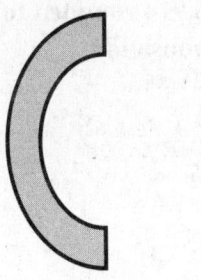

J

13 Which fraction represents the smallest part of a set?

A $\frac{1}{2}$

B $\frac{1}{4}$

C $\frac{1}{10}$

D $\frac{1}{8}$

14 Barry biked from his house to the library. He biked $3\frac{3}{4}$ miles. What is another way to write this distance?

F 3.25 miles

G 3.34 miles

H 3.43 miles

J 3.75 miles

15 Which of the following is *true*?

A $\frac{1}{3} = 1.3$

B $\frac{4}{5} > 3.5$

C $\frac{7}{2} > 3.5$

D $\frac{3}{8} < 0.45$

Name   Date

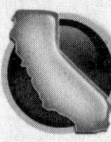 # Diagnostic Test (continued)

16 Which is equivalent to $\frac{9}{12}$?

   F $\frac{3}{6}$

   G $\frac{3}{4}$

   H $\frac{6}{9}$

   J $\frac{12}{15}$

17 Marisa wants to carpet her living room. Her living room is a rectangle with a width of 17 feet and a length of 22 feet. How much carpet will Marisa need to cover the floor of her living room?

   17 ft

   22 ft

   A 39 square feet

   B 78 square feet

   C 374 square feet

   D 748 square feet

18 Carter and Evie both ran a 200 meter dash. Carter's time was 29.38 seconds and Evie's time was 37.75 seconds. How much faster was Carter's time?

   F 8.37 seconds

   G 8.47 seconds

   H 12.43 seconds

   J 18.47 seconds

19 A school sold 282 adult tickets and 418 student tickets for a football game. About how many tickets were sold for the football game?

   A 300 tickets   **C** 600 tickets

   B 400 tickets   **D** 700 tickets

20 Natalie solved the problem below. Which expression could be used to check her answer?

$$4\overline{)2381} = 595r1$$

   F $(595 \times 4) + 1$

   G $(595 \times 1) + 4$

   H $(595 + 1) \times 4$

   J $(595 + 4) \times 1$

21 What is 8,256,914 rounded to the nearest ten-thousand?

   A 8,000,000

   B 8,250,000

   C 8,260,000

   D 8,300,000

22 The letters P and Q stand for numbers. If $P + 80 = Q + 80$, which statement is true?

   F $P > Q$

   G $P = Q$

   H $P < Q$

   J $P = Q + 80$

Diagnostic Test (continued)

23 The grid below shows 3 points that are all on the same straight line.

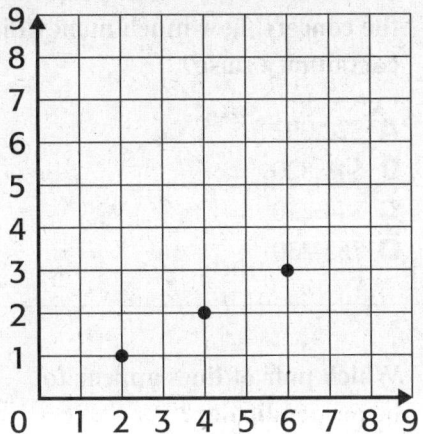

If another point is plotted on the line, what could be its coordinates?

A (1, 2)
B (8, 4)
C (7, 3)
D (8, 6)

24 Each week a teacher gives her class a quiz. Students can score a maximum of 10 points on each quiz. The table shows Jennifer's scores on the quizzes. What is the median of her scores?

Quiz	1	2	3	4	5	6	7
Score	10	7	8	6	10	10	8

F 6
G 7
H 8
J 10

25 $62{,}385 + 15{,}709 =$

A 46,676
B 77,084
C 77,094
D 78,094

26 Jocelyn marked her height on the growth chart below. What is Jocelyn's height in feet?

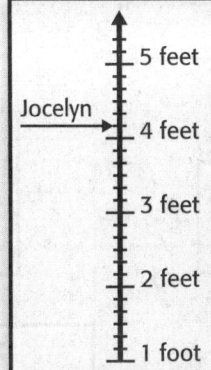

F $5\frac{5}{6}$ feet   **H** $4\frac{1}{5}$ feet

G $5\frac{1}{6}$ feet   **J** $4\frac{1}{6}$ feet

27 What number is represented by point Y on this number line?

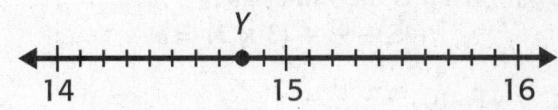

A 14.080
B 14.2
C 14.8
D 15.2

Name   Date

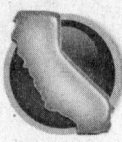
Diagnostic Test (continued)

28   14,508 + 6,281 =

   F 8,227
   G 10,789
   H 20,789
   J 77,310

29   Look at the rectangles below. Which rectangle has a perimeter of 18 and an area of 18?

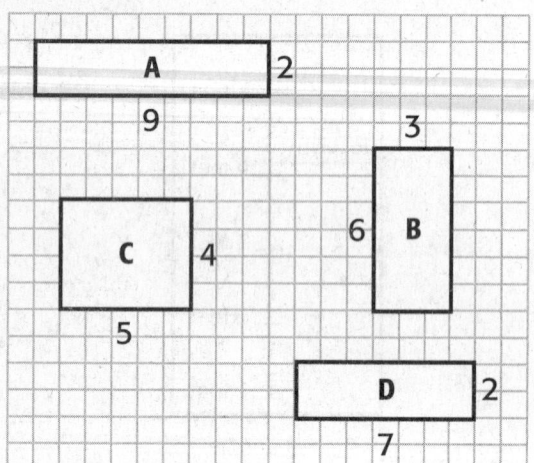

   A A
   B B
   C C
   D D

30   What is the value of b?
   $(45 \div 9) + (3 \times 2) = b$

   F 10
   G 11
   H 12
   J 16

31   A community held a concert to raise money for a new playground. Each ticket cost $15. If 3,682 people attended the concert, how much money did the community raise?

   A $22,092
   B $41,820
   C $44,230
   D $55,230

32   Which pair of lines appear to be perpendicular?

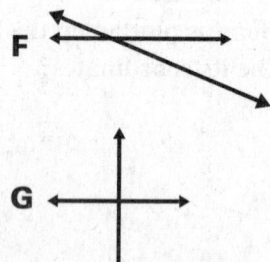
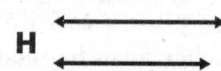
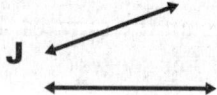

33   215
         × 27
        ——

   A 1,935
   B 5,675
   C 5,805
   D 7,005

Diagnostic Test (continued)

34 Nick plays the piano. If he spends 40 minutes each day practicing, how many minutes will Nick spend practicing the piano in a year? (1 year = 365 days)

   F 1,460 minutes
   G 12,400 minutes
   H 12,600 minutes
   J 14,600 minutes

35 Which list below has all the factors of 7?

   A 7
   B 1 and 7
   C 1, 3, 4, and 7
   D 1, 2, 3, 4, 5, and 6

36 Evaluate the expression below when $n = 2$.

$$n \times (7 + 8)$$

   F 13
   G 17
   H 22
   J 30

37 Which is a prime number?

   A 2
   B 9
   C 15
   D 21

38 Which fraction represents the shaded part of the figure?

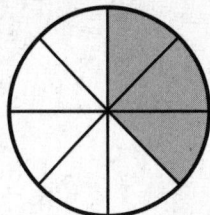

   F $\frac{3}{5}$ **H** $\frac{5}{8}$
   G $\frac{3}{8}$ **J** $\frac{5}{3}$

39 Look at the line segment shown below.

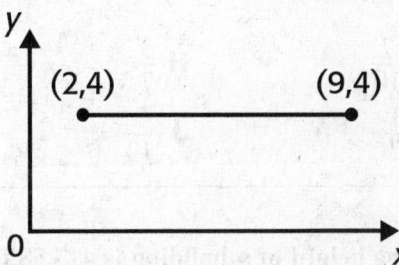

What is the length of the line segment?

   A 2 units
   B 5 units
   C 7 units
   D 11 units

40 Which of these is another way to write the product 14×3?

   F $1 \times 4 \times 3$
   G $7 \times 7 \times 3$
   H $2 \times 7 \times 3$
   J $3 \times 4 \times 3$

Diagnostic Test (continued)

41 Mrs. Bardo bought 8 tickets to the aquarium. She spent a total of $184. How much did each ticket cost?

    A $22
    B $23
    C $24
    D $25

42 On the number line below, what fraction does point *T* represent?

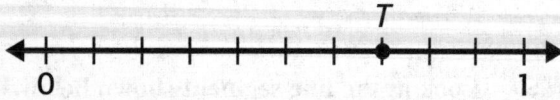

    F $\dfrac{7}{10}$ **H** $\dfrac{3}{7}$

    G $\dfrac{1}{7}$ **J** $\dfrac{3}{10}$

43 The height of a building is 413.58 feet. What is the height of the building rounded to the nearest whole number?

    A 400 feet
    B 410 feet
    C 413 feet
    D 414 feet

44 What is the value of the expression below?

$$(7 \times 8) - (22 + 13)$$

    F 19   **H** 45
    G 21   **J** 47

45 $382 \div 8 =$

    A 48
    B 47 R6
    C 45 R2
    D 42

46 Mr. Parson can drive his car 23 miles using one gallon of gas. The gas tank in his car holds 14 gallons of gas. How many miles can Mr. Parson drive on a full tank of gas?

    F 370 miles
    G 322 miles
    H 312 miles
    J 222 miles

47 In which equation does $x = 4$?

    A $7x = 21$
    B $24 \div x = 6$
    C $x - 13 = 17$
    D $25 + x = 39$

48 $$3 \times (7 + 2) =$$

    F 21
    G 23
    H 27
    J 42

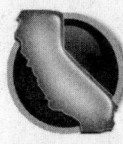

Diagnostic Test (continued)

49 There are 252 students in the school. Each classroom has the same number of students. If there are 9 classrooms, how many students are in each classroom?

A 26
B 27
C 28
D 29

50 Which equation can be used to find the area of this rectangle in square feet?

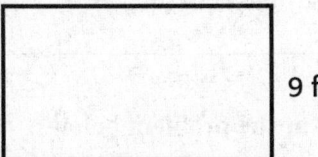

9 ft

16 ft

F $A = (2 \times 16) + (2 \times 9)$
G $A = (2 + 16) \times (2 + 9)$
H $A = 2 \times (16 \times 9)$
J $A = 16 \times 9$

51 The Torres family is driving to the beach. They have driven 56 miles of the 312 mile trip. Which number sentence below can be used to find how many miles the Torres family still needs to drive?

A $312 + 56 = \square$
B $\square - 56 = 312$
C $\square - 312 = 56$
D $312 - 56 = \square$

52 The difference of x minus y equals 15. If $x = 49$, which equation can be used to find the value of y?

F $x - 15 = 49$
G $49 - y = 15$
H $49 + 15 = y$
J $15 - y = 49$

53 Which of the following formulas can be used for the table below?

Input (x)	Output (y)
12	3
20	5
28	7
44	11

A $y = x - 9$
B $y = 4x$
C $y = x \div 4$
D $y = 9 + x$

54 What value of n makes this number sentence true?

$$6 \times n = 6 \times (9 - 5)$$

F 4
G 5
H 9
J 14

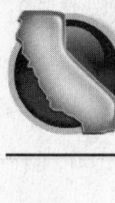

Diagnostic Test (continued)

55 A square has an area of 36 square feet. What is the length of each side?

A 4 feet
B 6 feet
C 9 feet
D 18 feet

56 Which best describes this triangle?

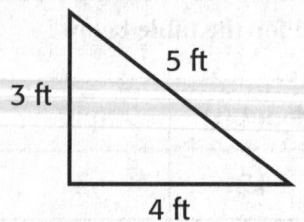

F equilateral
G isosceles
H scalene
J obtuse

57 Look at the problem below.

$$b = a + 5$$

If $a = 8$, what is b?

A 3   **C** 13
B 8   **D** 40

58 Angle R is an acute angle. Which could be the measure of angle R?

F 180°   **H** 90°
G 105°   **J** 45°

59 Which statement about the figures is true?

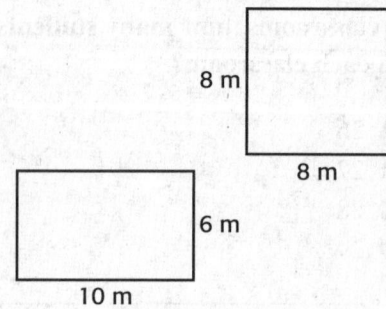

A They have the same perimeter.
B They have the same area.
C They have the same width.
D They are both squares.

60 Look at the problem below.

$$(5 - 2) \times \triangle = \bigcirc \times (18 \div 6)$$

What is the relationship between $\triangle$ and $\bigcirc$?

F $\triangle > \bigcirc$
G $\triangle < \bigcirc$
H $\triangle = \bigcirc$
J $3 \times \triangle = \bigcirc$

61 Which number is represented by a?

$$6 \times a = 192$$

A 32   **C** 34
B 33   **D** 42

Diagnostic Test (continued)

62 Read each of the statements below.

#1 All rectangles are squares.

#2 All rectangles are parallelograms.

#3 All squares are rhombuses.

Which of the statement(s) are *true*?

F Only statement #2
G Statement #1 and #2
H Statement #2 and #3
J Statement #1, #2, and #3

63 On a coordinate grid, Point *A* is at
(7, 13) and Point *C* is at (7, 4).
What is the length of the line segment
that connects Point *A* to Point *C*?

A 6 units   **C** 11 units
B 9 units   **D** 17 units

64 Look at the circle below.

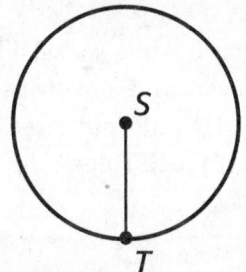

The line segment *ST* appears to be:

F the center
G the diameter
H a chord
J the radius

65 Mr. Walton has a stone patio in
his backyard. Here is a diagram of
the patio.

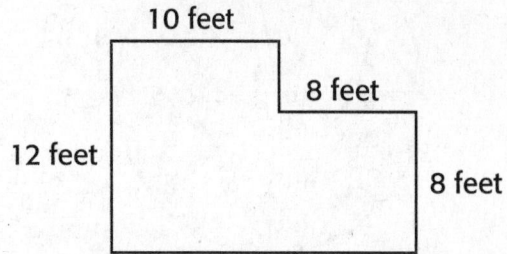

What is the area of the patio?

A 38 square feet
B 56 square feet
C 60 square feet
D 184 square feet

66 Tommy and Mary signed up for the
Read-a-Thon. The bar graph shows
the number of books the students read
each week.

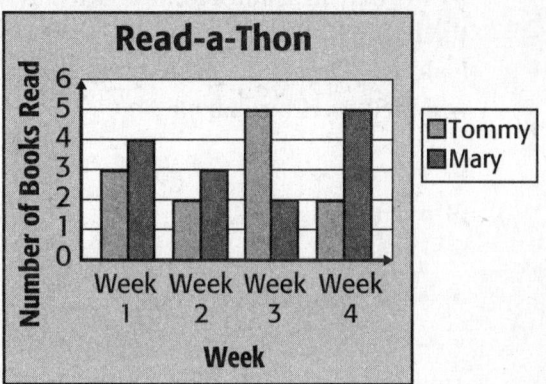

How many books did Tommy read over
the four weeks?

F 9 books   **H** 14 books
G 12 books   **J** 26 books

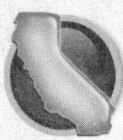

Diagnostic Test (continued)

67 Look at this spinner.

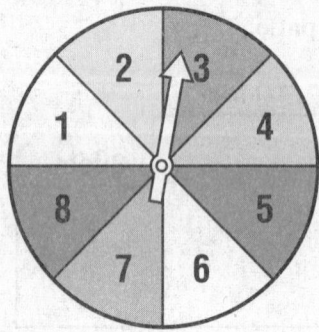

How many outcomes are possible if you spin the spinner and toss a two-sided coin?

A 8
B 10
C 16
D 32

68 Micah has a bag of marbles that are all the same size. He has 5 red marbles, 3 blue marbles, and 4 yellow marbles in the bag. Micah pulls a marble without looking. What is the probability that he will pick a yellow marble?

F 1 out of 3
G 4 out of 8
H 1 out of 4
J 1 out of 1

69 What type of symmetry does this figure have?

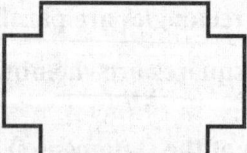

A only bilateral symmetry
B only rotational symmetry
C rotational and bilateral symmetry
D The figure does not have symmetry.

70 Which expression goes in the box to make this number sentence true?

$$8 + 28 = \square + 28$$

F 4×2
G 2×2
H $4 + 2$
J $2 + 2$

71 Hugo has 8 white socks, 4 black socks, 2 red socks, and 6 brown socks in a drawer. He pulls out a sock without looking. Which color is he most likely to pull?

A white
B black
C red
D brown

Diagnostic Test (continued)

72 Look at the map. Which expression can you use to find the distance between the library and the school?

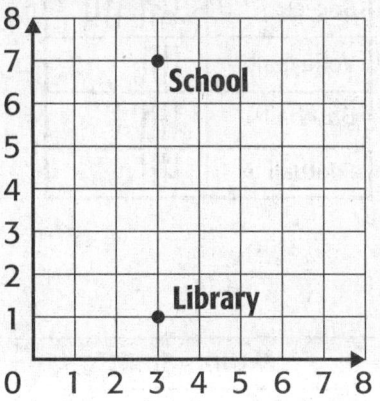

F $7 - 1$ **H** $3 + 7$
G $1 + 7$ **J** $7 - 3$

73 Look at the figures below. Which figures appear to be congruent?

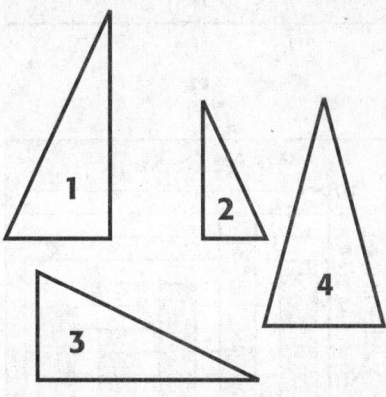

A 1 and 2
B 1 and 3
C 1, 2, and 3
D None of the figures are congruent.

74 What is the mode of this set of data?

$$\{4, 4, 5, 6, 8, 10, 12\}$$

F 4
G 6
H 7
J 8

75 The line graph shows the estimated sales at a toy store over the past five years.

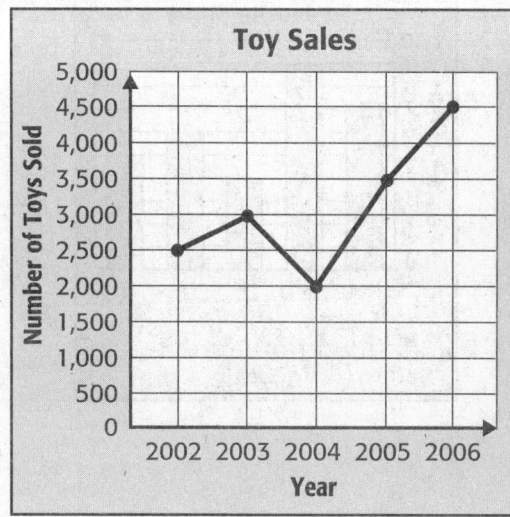

About how many more toys were sold in 2006 than 2004?

A 1,000 toys
B 1,500 toys
C 2,000 toys
D 2,500 toys

Diagnostic Test (continued)

76 Wendy surveyed students about their favorite sport. She recorded the results in this tally table.

Favorite Sport	
Basketball	卌 ‖
Soccer	卌 ‖‖
Volleyball	‖‖
Baseball	卌 ‖
Football	卌

Which bar graph shows the results of Wendy's survey?

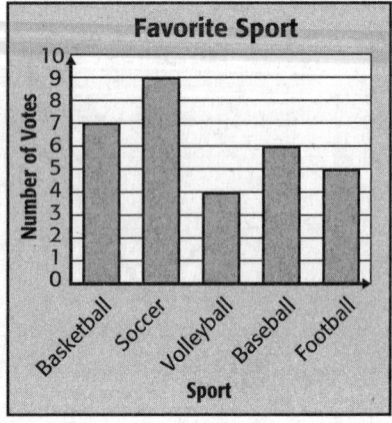

F

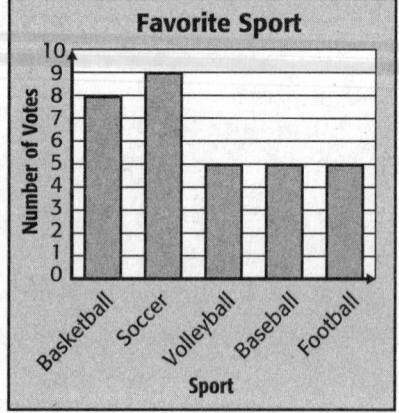

H

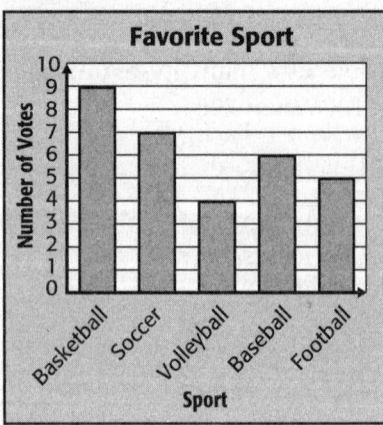

G

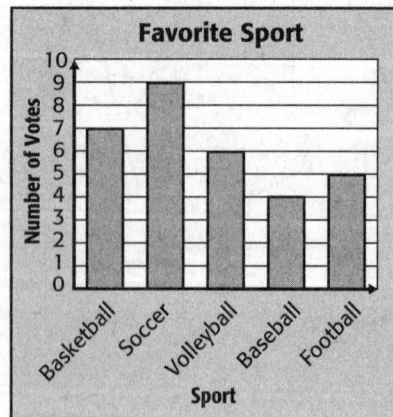

J

Stop

Workspace

Workspace

Name _____ Date _____

Practice by Standard
Number Sense 1.1

4NS1.1 **Read and write whole numbers in the millions.**

1 Which of these is the word form of 3,450,023?

A three million, four hundred fifty, twenty-three

B three million, forty-five thousand, twenty-three

C three million, four hundred fifty thousand, twenty-three

D three billion, forty-five million, twenty-three thousand

2 The population of a city is six hundred thirty-three thousand, nine hundred eighty-four. Which of the following is the population in standard form?

F 633,000

G 633,900

H 633,984

J 633,984,000

3 Which of the following is equivalent to 400,000 + 23,000 + 45?

A 423,450

B 423,045

C 423,000

D 400,045

4 The diameter of the planet Saturn is about 74,900 miles. Which number is 10,000 less than Saturn's diameter?

F 64,900

G 73,900

H 74,800

J 74,890

5 $200,000 + 13 =$

A 200,013

B 200,130

C 201,300

D 213,000

6 The budget of the city recycling department is $2,345,106. What is the expanded form of this number?

F 2,000,000 + 30,000 + 4,000 + 500 + 10 + 6

G 2,000,000 + 300,000 + 4,000 + 5,000 + 100 + 6

H 2,000,000 + 300,000 + 40,000 + 5,000 + 100 + 6

J 2,000,000 + 300,000 + 40,000 + 5,000 + 1,000 + 6

Practice by Standard
Number Sense 1.1 (continued)

7 A city buys a piece of property for $1,236,734. Which number is in the ten thousands place?

A 2
B 3
C 6
D 7

8 Which of the following has 3 in the hundreds place?

F 23,458
G 34,882
H 645,139
J 880,340

9 Which of these is the word form of 560,000?

A five hundred six
B five hundred sixty
C five hundred six thousand
D five hundred sixty thousand

10 Which of the following is 2,000,000 less than 8 million, 26 thousand, 26?

F 6 million, 24 thousand, 26
G 6 million, 26 thousand, 24
H 6 million, 26 thousand, 26
J 8 million, 26 thousand, 24

11 Which of the following is equivalent to 20,000,000 + 5,000,000 + 30,000 + 5,000 + 60 +7?

A five million, thirty-five thousand, sixty-seven
B twenty million, five hundred thirty-five thousand, sixty-seven
C twenty-five million, three thousand five hundred sixty-seven
D twenty-five million, thirty-five thousand, sixty-seven

12 Which of the following has 7 in the ten millions place?

F 357,000,312
G 472,456,210
H 762,28,010
J 956,871,203

13 Which of these is the word form of 8,964,021?

A eight million, nine hundred sixty-four thousand, two hundred one
B eight million, nine hundred sixty-four, twenty-one
C eight billion, nine hundred sixty-four thousand, two hundred one
D eight million, nine hundred sixty-four thousand, twenty-one

Practice by Standard
Number Sense 1.2

4NS1.2 Order and compare whole numbers and decimals to two decimal places.

1 Which of the following has the least value?

A 4.5
B 3.1
C 5.6
D 0.4

2 The Science Club at school is raising money to buy lab equipment. The table shows the amount of money raised by the members. Who raised the most money?

Student	Amount Raised
Julie	$23.67
Michel	$35.09
Manuela	$27.98
Xiang	$36.11

F Julie
G Michel
H Manuela
J Xiang

3 Which of the following orders the set of numbers from greatest to least?

345,891; 381,042; 389,934; 386,000; 310,450

A 310,450; 345,891; 381,042; 386,000; 389,934
B 389,934; 386,000; 381,042; 310,450; 345,891
C 389,934; 386,000; 381,042; 345,891; 310,450
D 386,000; 389,934; 381,042; 310,450; 345,891

4 Which of the following is not true?

F $3.4 < 3.41$
G $11.4 > 11.38$
H $7.98 > 8$
J $4.77 < 4.97$

5 Which of the following has the greatest value?

A 113.45
B 113.87
C 113.56
D 113.02

Name _____ Date _____

Practice by Standard
Number Sense 1.3

4NS1.3 Round whole numbers through the millions to the nearest ten, hundred, thousand, ten thousand, or hundred thousand.

Use the table to answer Questions 1 and 2.

Country	Area (sq mi)
Brazil	3,286,470
Canada	3,855,081
China	3,705,386
United States	3,537,438

1 What is the area of the United States rounded to the nearest thousand square miles?

A 3,500,000 square miles
B 3,537,000 square miles
C 3,540,000 square miles
D 3,705,000 square miles

2 Which countries have an area less than 3,600,000 square miles when rounded to the nearest hundred thousand?

F Brazil, Canada, China, United States
G Canada, China, United States
H Canada, China
J Brazil, United States

3 What is 34,445,230 rounded to the nearest ten thousand?

A 34,400,000
B 34,440,000
C 34,445,000
D 34,450,000

4 A number rounded to the nearest hundred thousand is written as 2,300,000. Which of the following could be that number?

F 2,321,363
G 2,358,300
H 2,361,334
J 2,371,563

5 Round 456,238,910 to the nearest ten thousand. How many zeros are in your answer?

A 2 zeros
B 3 zeros
C 4 zeros
D 5 zeros

Name _____ Date _____

Practice by Standard
Number Sense 1.5 and 1.6

4NS1.5 Explain different interpretations of fractions, for example, parts of a whole, parts of a set, and division of whole numbers by whole numbers; explain equivalents of fractions.

1 Which fraction represents the smallest part of a whole?

A $\frac{2}{5}$

B $\frac{3}{5}$

C $\frac{4}{5}$

D $\frac{1}{5}$

2 A group of students has 4 boys and 2 girls. What fraction names the number of boys in the group?

F $\frac{2}{6}$

G $\frac{2}{4}$

H $\frac{4}{6}$

J $\frac{4}{2}$

3 6 out of 8 boys =

A $\frac{3}{4}$

B $\frac{4}{3}$

C 2

D 68

4NS1.6 Write tenths and hundredths in decimal and fraction notations and know the fraction and decimal equivalents for halves and fourths (e.g., $\frac{1}{2} = 0.5$ or .50; $\frac{7}{4} = 1\frac{3}{4} = 1.75$).

1 Which decimal represents the shaded part of the picture?

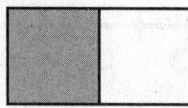

A 0.1

B 0.4

C 0.5

D 0.7

2 Which fraction means the same as 0.29?

F $\frac{29}{1000}$

G $\frac{29}{100}$

H $\frac{29}{10}$

J $\frac{29}{1}$

3 $1\frac{1}{2} =$

A 1.1

B 1.2

C 1.25

D 1.5

Practice by Standard
Number Sense 1.7

4NS1.7 Write the fraction represented by a drawing of parts of a figure; represent a given fraction by using drawings; and relate a fraction to a simple decimal on a number line.

1 What fraction is best represented by point *A* on this number line?

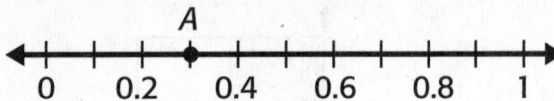

A $\frac{1}{10}$

B $\frac{3}{10}$

C $\frac{2}{5}$

D $\frac{8}{10}$

2 Which fraction represents the shaded part of this picture?

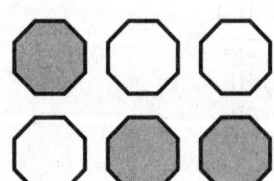

F $\frac{1}{6}$

G $\frac{1}{3}$

H $\frac{3}{6}$

J $\frac{3}{3}$

3 Which shaded part represents the fraction $\frac{3}{4}$?

A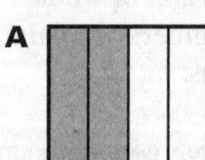

B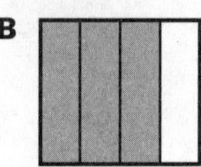

C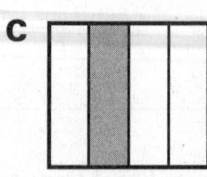

D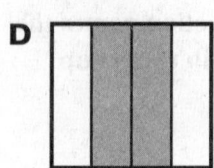

4 Which fraction represents the un-shaded part of this picture?

F $\frac{0}{3}$ **H** $\frac{2}{3}$

G $\frac{1}{3}$ **J** $\frac{3}{3}$

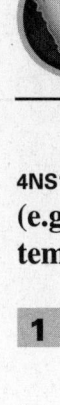

Practice by Standard
Number Sense 1.8

4NS1.8 Use concepts of negative numbers (e.g., on a number line, in counting, in temperature, in "owing").

1 Which symbol is located at ⁻5 on the number line below?

A ◇

B ♡

C ☺

D ▢

---

2 Which number best represents thirty feet below sea level?

F ⁻35

G ⁻30

H 0

J 30

---

3 Of this set of integers, which has the least value?

$$4, \,^-5, \, 12, \,^-12, \,^-6$$

A 12

B ⁻5

C ⁻12

D 4

---

4 The numbers in the pattern increase by the same amount each time. What are the next three numbers in this pattern?

$$^-34, \,^-31, \,^-28, \,^-25, \, \_\_, \, \_\_, \, \_\_$$

F ⁻28, ⁻31, ⁻34

G ⁻22, ⁻19, ⁻16

H 28, 31, 34

J 22, 19, 16

---

5 Mrs. Harper withdraws $75 from her savings account and then deposits $45 into her checking account. Which integer represents the amount of her withdrawal?

A ⁻75

B ⁻45

C 30

D 75

Practice by Standard
Number Sense 1.8 (continued)

6 Order the integers from least to greatest.

−30, −24, −47, −23, −45

F −47, −45, −30, −24, −23
G −23, −24, −30, −45, −47
H −24, −23, −30, −47, −45
J −47, −45, −30, −23, −24

7 In a football game, a team gained 16 yards in its first play. In its second play, it lost 18 yards. Which number represents the team's total gain or loss in yards after the two plays?

A −34
B −2
C 2
D 24

8 Which statement is true?

F −4 < −6
G −5 > 0
H −12 < −7
J −7 > −4

9 The temperature on a spring day changed from 56°F at 1:00 P.M. to 46°F at 8:00 P.M. Which integer represents the change in temperature from 1:00 P.M. to 8:00 P.M.?

A −46
B −10
C 10
D 46

10 The numbers in a pattern are shown below. Which of the following statements describes the pattern?

−67, −72, −77, −82, −87

F Add five.
G Subtract five.
H Multiply by five.
J Divide by five.

11 Which symbol is located at −2 on the number line below?

A △

B ☾

C ☺

D ♡

12 Which statement is true?

F −6 < −3
G −9 < −10
H −15 > −13
J −20 > 0

Practice by Standard
Number Sense 1.9

4NS1.9 Identify on a number line the relative position of positive fractions, positive mixed numbers, and positive decimals to two decimal places.

1 What fraction is best represented by point *G* on this number line?

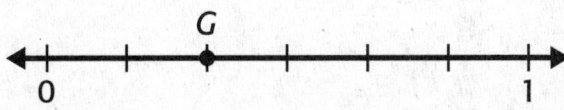

- **A** $\frac{1}{6}$
- **B** $\frac{1}{3}$
- **C** $\frac{1}{2}$
- **D** $\frac{5}{6}$

2 Which number best represents point *A* on this number line?

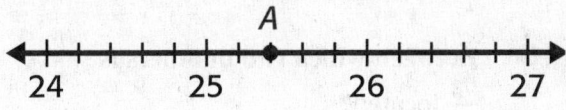

- **F** $25\frac{2}{5}$
- **G** $25\frac{3}{5}$
- **H** $25\frac{27}{5}$
- **J** $25\frac{2}{26}$

3 On the number line below, what point represents $1\frac{1}{3}$?

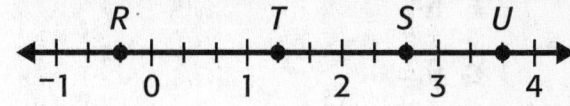

- **A** *R*
- **B** *T*
- **C** *S*
- **D** *U*

4 Which point represents the number 0.6?

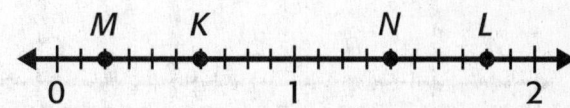

- **F** *M*
- **G** *K*
- **H** *N*
- **J** *L*

5 Between which two numbers does 1.78 fall on a number line?

- **A** 7 and 8
- **B** 1.7 and 1.8
- **C** 1.8 and 2.0
- **D** 1.7 and 1.5

Practice by Standard
Number Sense 1.9 (continued)

6 Which number is located to the right of 16.5 on a number line?

F $16\frac{3}{8}$

G $16\frac{2}{6}$

H $16\frac{5}{8}$

J $16\frac{7}{16}$

7 Which number line represents point A as $53\frac{1}{4}$, point B as $55\frac{1}{2}$, and point C as 58.75?

A

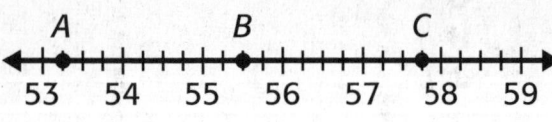

B

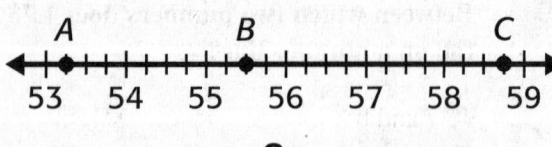

C

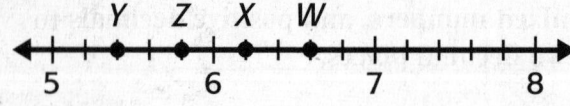

D

8 Which point represents 5.80?

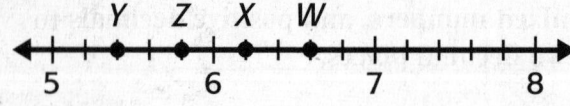

F Y

G Z

H X

J W

9 On a number line, which number is located to the left of $3\frac{3}{5}$?

A $3\frac{1}{2}$

B $3\frac{3}{4}$

C $3\frac{7}{8}$

D $3\frac{9}{10}$

10 Between which two numbers is $\frac{73}{7}$ located?

F 8 and 9

G 9 and 10

H 10 and 11

J 11 and 12

Practice by Standard
Number Sense 2.1

4NS2.1 **Estimate and compute the sum or difference of whole numbers and positive decimals to two places.**

1   687 − 341 =

A ⁻346

B 346

C 926

D 1028

2   Adam bought the items in the table below. Approximately how much did he spend?

Item	Price
Mangos	$7.15
Bread	$5.54
Pencils	$2.78

F $12

G $14

H $15

J $16

3   During one week, Mrs. Cooper drove the following distances. Which is a reasonable estimate for the total number of miles she drove?

Day	Distance (in miles)
Sunday	12
Monday	45
Tuesday	73
Wednesday	169
Thursday	7
Friday	24
Saturday	99

A 260 miles

B 310 miles

C 430 miles

D 530 miles

4   Hector had $20.00. He spent $12.56 on a book at the bookstore. How much money does Hector have left?

F $7.44

G $7.54

H $18.54

J $32.56

Practice by Standard
Number Sense 2.2

4NS2.2 **Round two-place decimals to one decimal or the nearest whole number and judge the reasonableness of the rounded answer.**

1 Mr. Jones buys a telephone for $53.99 and 4 cans of paint for $62.40. What is a reasonable estimate of his total cost?

   A $54

   B $60

   C $114

   D $116

2 A store sells carpet for $31 per square foot. The Rodriguez family buys 45 square feet of carpet. Estimate their total cost of the carpet.

   F $80

   G $150

   H $1000

   J $1500

3 The length of fencing needed for a yard is 457.56 feet. What is the length of the fencing rounded to the nearest tenth of a foot?

   A 457 feet

   B 457.5 feet

   C 457.6 feet

   D 458 feet

4 The length of the wheelbase of a truck is 225.34 inches. What is the length rounded to the nearest inch?

   F 225 inches

   G 225.3 inches

   H 225.35 inches

   J 226 inches

5 An orange has about 63 calories. Gloria eats 2 oranges a day for 17 days. Estimate the number of calories in all of the oranges she eats.

   A 120 calories

   B 126 calories

   C 1200 calories

   D 2400 calories

6 A landscaper can dig a hole to plant a tree in about 18 minutes. About how long will it take him to dig 18 holes?

   F 40 minutes

   G 100 minutes

   H 180 minutes

   J 400 minutes

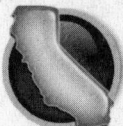

Practice by Standard
Number Sense 3.1

4NS3.1 **Demonstrate an understanding of, and the ability to use, standard algorithms for the addition and subtraction of multidigit numbers.**

1 Mr. Wong is shopping for a computer. One computer costs $1250 and another computer costs $988. What is the difference in price between the two computers?

- **A** $262
- **B** $272
- **C** $362
- **D** $2238

2 Carmen is saving money for a digital camera. If she has already saved $150, which of the following expressions will tell her how much money she still needs?

- **F** $349 \div 150$
- **G** $349 - 150$
- **H** $349 + 150$
- **J** 349×150

3 $13{,}401 + 2369 - 1223 =$

- **A** 9809
- **B** 12,255
- **C** 14,547
- **D** 16,993

---

4 The table below represents the number of inches an insect flew on three days. How many total inches did the insect fly on the three days combined?

Day	Number of Inches
Monday	7267
Wednesday	2450
Thursday	4852

- **F** 9717 inches
- **G** 12,119 inches
- **H** 14,569 inches
- **J** 14,570 inches

---

5 James is adding 4578 and 4666. Which statement is true?

- **A** The sum of the two numbers is more than 10,000.
- **B** The sum of the two numbers is less than 8000.
- **C** The digit in the ones place of the sum is 4.
- **D** The digit in the hundreds place of the sum is greater than 3.

Practice by Standard
Number Sense 3.1 (continued)

6 A state forest has 5267 acres. Of the forest, 301 acres are reserved for recreational activities and 250 acres are reserved for camping. How many acres of the forest are left?

F 551 acres

G 4716 acres

H 4966 acres

J 5017 acres

7 A salesman earned $3567 in sales income last month. He paid $249 in income taxes. How much money does he have left?

A $3316

B $3318

C $3322

D $3328

8 The table below represents the monthly attendance at a university's basketball games. How many more people attended in November than in January?

Month	Attendance
November	17,502
December	15,340
January	11,320

F 2162 people

G 4020 people

H 6182 people

J 28,882 people

9 A car dealership had 4536 cars at the lot on Monday. They sold 21 cars on Tuesday and 54 cars on Wednesday. Then on Thursday they added 72 cars to the lot. On Friday, they sold 31 more cars. How many cars were at the dealership on Saturday?

A 4175 cars

B 4358 cars

C 4502 cars

D 4533 cars

10 $34,692 + 51,989 =$

F 86,681

G 86,671

H 85,571

J 83,581

11 Travis visited an art museum with his fourth grade class. There were 2354 artworks in the museum. If Travis saw 562 paintings, how many artworks does he have left to see?

A 2816

B 2212

C 1892

D 1792

Name   Date

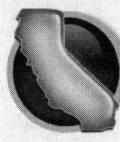

Practice by Standard
Number Sense 3.2

4NS3.2 Demonstrate an understanding of, and the ability to use, standard algorithms for multiplying a multidigit number by a two-digit number and for dividing a multidigit number by a one-digit number; use relationships between them to simplify computations and to check results.

1 Mrs. Kirby needs to save $576 for a new television. She has 8 months to save for the television. How much should she save each month?

    A $71
    B $72
    C $73
    D $74

2 Divide 2390 by 6. What is the remainder?

    F 1
    G 2
    H 3
    J 4

3 Benji has a 450 page novel to read for his class. He has finished 266 pages. If he has 8 days to finish the novel, how many pages must he read each day?

    A 23
    B 33
    C 56
    D 89

4 Kelly solved the problem below. Which expression could be used to check her answer?

$$5789 \div 9 = 643r2$$

    F $(643 \times 2) + 9$
    G $(643 + 9) \times 2$
    H $(643 \times 9) + 2$
    J $(643 + 2) \times 9$

5 Oscar is multiplying 5345 by 7. What is the number 7 called?

    A product
    B factor
    C addend
    D dividend

6 Which division problem corresponds to the expression $(45 \times 4) + 1$?

    F $4)\overline{181}$ $45r1$
    G $4)\overline{181}$ $45r3$
    H $4)\overline{180}$ $4r45$
    J $4)\overline{181}$ $45r4$

Name   Date

Practice by Standard
Number Sense 3.2 (continued)

7 Which number goes in the box in the division problem below?

$$5\overline{)923}$$ with quotient $1\square$, 5, 42

A 6
B 7
C 8
D 9

8 An office building has 168 windows. Each floor has the same number of windows. The building has 7 floors. How do you find the number of windows on each floor?

F Divide 7 by 168.
G Subtract 7 from 168.
H Multiply 168 and 7.
J Divide 168 by 7.

9 $782 \div 4 =$

A 181 r 58
B 195
C 195 r 2
D 218 r 3

10 The Norelli family has donated the same amount of money to the local library each year for the past 6 years. The total amount given each year was $120. How much money did the Norelli family give over the 6 years?

F $126
G $160
H $720
J $810

11 There are 405 cans of soup packed into 9 cases. How many cans of soup are in each case?

A 20
B 25
C 40
D 45

12 Which of the following correctly explains how to check the division problem below?

$$8\overline{)3417}$$ with quotient $427r1$

F Multiply 427 and 8 and then add 3417.
G Multiply 427 and 1 and then add 8.
H Multiply 427 and 8 and then add 1.
J Multiply 1 and 8 and then add 3417.

Practice by Standard
Number Sense 3.3

4NS3.3 Solve problems involving multiplication of multidigit numbers by two-digit numbers.

1 $43 \times 135 =$

    A 92
    B 178
    C 4595
    D 5805

2 How many zeros does the product of 20 and 1000 have?

    F 2
    G 3
    H 4
    J 5

3 There are 32 buses for a school field trip. If each bus can carry 25 people, how many people can go on the field trip?

    A 800
    B 790
    C 645
    D 57

4 Tobias is calculating the problem below. What should he do next?

$$\begin{array}{r} \overset{2}{2340} \\ \times\ \ 15 \\ \hline 00 \end{array}$$

    F Multiply 3 and 2. Then add 3.
    G Multiply 3 and 5. Then add 1.
    H Multiply 2 and 5. Then add 3.
    J Multiply 3 and 5. Then add 2.

5 Mr. Orta buys 12 gallons of paint. Each gallon of paint costs $33. How much does he pay for the 12 gallons of paint?

    A $332
    B $356
    C $396
    D $399

6 Which digit is in the ones place of the product for 72×410?

    F 0
    G 2
    H 5
    J 9

Practice by Standard
Number Sense 3.3 (continued)

7 Which number goes in the boxed row?

$$
\begin{array}{r}
11 \\
375 \\
\times \quad 52 \\
\hline
750 \\
\boxed{} \\
\hline
19,500
\end{array}
$$

- **A** 18,600
- **B** 18,650
- **C** 18,750
- **D** 19,750

8 Mrs. Howard works 35 hours a week. She is paid $25 an hour. How much money does she make in one week?

- **F** $675
- **G** $855
- **H** $875
- **J** $955

9 $45 \times 45 =$

- **A** 2000
- **B** 2020
- **C** 2025
- **D** 2035

10 Which number is the product of 127 and 10?

- **F** 120
- **G** 1207
- **H** 1270
- **J** 12,700

11 What is the first step to finding the product of the problem below?

$$
\begin{array}{r}
103 \\
\times \quad 23
\end{array}
$$

- **A** Multiply 0 and 2.
- **B** Multiply 0 and 3.
- **C** Multiply 3 and 2.
- **D** Multiply 3 and 3.

12 $1005 \times 20 =$

- **F** 1010
- **G** 2010
- **H** 20,100
- **J** 201,000

Practice by Standard
Number Sense 3.4

4NS3.4 Solve problems involving division of multidigit numbers by one-digit divisors.

1 There are 405 seats in a school auditorium. Each row seats 9 students. How many rows of seats does the auditorium have?

A 34
B 45
C 49
D 55

2 Michaela is keeping a journal for her English class. She needs to write 162 pages by the end of the school year. If the school year is nine months long, how many pages should she write each month?

F 18
G 20
H 21
J 22

3 $345 \div 8 =$

A 41 R7
B 42 R9
C 43
D 43 R1

4 A case of notebook paper has 2500 sheets of paper. There are 5 notebooks in the case. How many sheets of paper are in each notebook?

F 50
G 100
H 500
J 550

5 The science club sold 140 calendars for a fund–raiser. There are 7 members in the club. If each member sold the same number of calendars, how many calendars did each person sell?

A 10
B 15
C 20
D 30

6 Matt has 5 shelves in his room that display 75 model cars. If each shelf holds the same number of cars, how many cars are on each shelf?

F 10
G 15
H 20
J 25

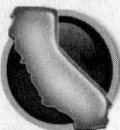

Practice by Standard
Number Sense 3.4 (continued)

7 Divide 672 by 3. What is the remainder?

- **A** 0
- **B** 1
- **C** 2
- **D** 3

8 Which number goes in the box in the division problem below?

$$
\begin{array}{r}
4\square \\
5\overline{)241} \\
\underline{20} \\
41
\end{array}
$$

- **F** 5
- **G** 7
- **H** 8
- **J** 9

9 There are 270 cars in the school parking lot. There are 6 cars in each row. How many rows of cars are in the parking lot?

- **A** 45
- **B** 47
- **C** 49
- **D** 51

10 Jaime's swimming lessons cost $150 each summer. If the lessons last 3 months, how much money does Jaime pay each month?

- **F** $25
- **G** $40
- **H** $49
- **J** $50

11 What is the value of the digit that goes in the box?

$$
\begin{array}{r}
\square 01 \\
5\overline{)4505}
\end{array}
$$

- **A** 8
- **B** 9
- **C** 10
- **D** 11

12 Mrs. Orlando has 224 boxes of pencils for all the classes in her school. Each class gets 8 boxes of pencils. How many classes are in the school?

- **F** 26
- **G** 28
- **H** 30
- **J** 32

Name _____ Date _____

 # Practice by Standard
Number Sense 4.1 and 4.2

4NS4.1 **Understand that many whole numbers break down in different ways (e.g., $12 = 4 \times 3 = 2 \times 6 = 2 \times 2 \times 3$).**

1 Which expression is equal to 4×14?

   A 7×2
   B 4×7
   C $2 \times 2 \times 2 \times 7$
   D $2 \times 2 \times 2 \times 2 \times 7$

2 Which of these is another way to write 72?

   F $2 \times 2 \times 3$
   G $2 \times 2 \times 2 \times 3$
   H $8 \times 3 \times 3$
   J $8 \times 2 \times 5$

3 Which of the following is *not* equivalent to 36?

   A 4×9
   B 18×2
   C $6 \times 2 \times 3$
   D 3×13

4NS4.2 **Know that numbers such as 2, 3, 5, 7, and 11 do not have any factors except 1 and themselves and that such numbers are called prime numbers.**

1 Which is *not* a prime number?

   A 13
   B 23
   C 45
   D 71

2 Which statement is true?

   F The only factors of 14 are 1 and 14.
   G The only factors of 5 are 1 and 5.
   H 16 is a prime number.
   J 9 is a prime number.

3 Which is a prime number?

   A 8
   B 21
   C 31
   D 42

Name   Date

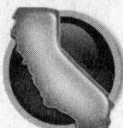

Practice by Standard
Algebra and Functions 1.1

4AF1.1 Use letters, boxes, or other symbols to stand for any number in simple expressions or equations (e.g., demonstrate an understanding and the use of the concept of a variable).

1 What number is represented by *s*?

$$4 \times s = 164$$

A 40
B 41
C 160
D 656

2 Mr. Angelo has 5 cases of bottled water. Each case holds 24 bottles. If *b* represents the total number of bottles in all the cases, which equation will help Mr. Angelo find the total number of water bottles?

F $b \times 5 = 24$

G $24 \times 5 = b$

H $b = \dfrac{24}{5}$

J $24 \div 5 = b$

3 Which expression is equivalent to the phrase *four more than r*?

A $r \div 4$
B $r - 4$
C $r + 4$
D $r \times 4$

4 Antonia earns $13 an hour. Last week she earned $585. If *h* is the number of hours she worked last week, which equation will help her solve for *h*?

F $h \neq 585 - 13$
G $h \times 13 = 585$
H $h \div 585 = 13$
J $h \times 585 = 13$

5 What is the value of $\square$?

$$\square + 23 = 44$$

A 18
B 21
C 24
D 67

6 How do you find the value of *k*?

$$k - 130 = 200$$

F Divide 200 by 130.
G Subtract 130 from 200.
H Add 200 and 130.
J Multiply 200 and 130.

Name   Date

Practice by Standard
Algebra and Functions 1.2

4AF1.2 Interpret and evaluate mathematical expressions that now use parentheses.

1 What is the value of the expression below?

$$(45 \div 9) \times 11$$

- **A** 33
- **B** 44
- **C** 55
- **D** 60

2 What is the value of the expression below if $k = 6$?

$$(72 \div 6) + (8 \times k)$$

- **F** 20
- **G** 26
- **H** 60
- **J** 72

3 $(48 \div 6) \times (2 + 1)$

- **A** 24
- **B** 36
- **C** 48
- **D** 60

4 What is the value of the expression below?

$$(32 \div 8) + (3 \times 3)$$

- **F** 5
- **G** 10
- **H** 13
- **J** 14

5 Which of the following correctly evaluates the expression below?

$$(36 \div 9) \times (11 - 6)$$

- **A** 10
- **B** 15
- **C** 20
- **D** 24

6 What is the value of the expression below?

$$5 \times (56 \div 8)$$

- **F** 25
- **G** 35
- **H** 40
- **J** 42

Practice by Standard
Algebra and Functions 1.2 (continued)

7 What is the value of the expression below?

$$(44 - 34) - (49 \div 7)$$

A 2
B 3
C 8
D 9

8 What is the value of the expression below?

$$10 \times (56 \div 8)$$

F 7
G 10
H 70
J 700

9 What is the value of the expression below?

$$(4 \times 2) + (18 \div 9)$$

A 10
B 16
C 72
D 80

10 $(15 - 4) - (2 + 8)$

F 0
G 1
H 3
J 5

11 Simplify the expression below.

$$(7 \times 3) - (64 \div 8)$$

A 2
B 8
C 13
D 21

12 Find the value of the expression below.

$$(5 \times 10) + (4 \times 10)$$

F 20
G 54
H 90
J 100

13 $(5 \times 4) + (3 \times 8)$

A 23
B 24
C 44
D 88

14 What is the value of the expression below?

$$(5 \times 5) + (6 \times 6)$$

F 25
G 36
H 50
J 61

Practice by Standard
Algebra and Functions 1.3

4AF1.3 Use parentheses to indicate which operation to perform first when writing expressions containing more than two terms and different operations.

1 What is the value of the expression below?

$$(7 - 3) \times 8$$

- **A** 17
- **B** 24
- **C** 32
- **D** 56

2 $(60 \div 5) + (8 \times 2)$

- **F** 12
- **G** 16
- **H** 20
- **J** 28

3 What is the value of the expression below?

$$7 \times (40 \div 8)$$

- **A** 5
- **B** 12
- **C** 35
- **D** 42

4 What is the value of the expression below?

$$(27 + 8) \div (9 - 4)$$

- **F** 5
- **G** 7
- **H** 30
- **J** 40

5 What is the value of the expression below?

$$(72 \div 8) \times (20 - 12)$$

- **A** 9
- **B** 17
- **C** 64
- **D** 72

6 $(48 \div 12) \times 6$

- **F** 4
- **G** 18
- **H** 24
- **J** 30

Practice by Standard
Algebra and Functions 1.3 (continued)

7 What is the value of the expression below?

$$15 \times (50 \div 10)$$

A 5
B 10
C 55
D 75

8 $(38 - 24) + (16 \div 4)$

F 4
G 14
H 18
J 28

9 What is the value of the expression below?

$$(4 \times 3) \times (27 \div 9)$$

A 3
B 12
C 36
D 48

10 $(18 \div 3) - (3 + 3)$

F 0
G 3
H 6
J 12

11 What is the value of the expression below?

$$(5 \times 5) - (30 \div 5)$$

A 6
B 19
C 25
D 31

12 Which of the following correctly simplifies the expression below?

$$(7 \times 11) + (2 \times 11)$$

F 22
G 77
H 88
J 99

13 $(9 \times 9) - (4 \times 8)$

A 32
B 49
C 81
D 113

14 What is the value of the expression below?

$$(5 \times 4) + 16$$

F 16
G 20
H 36
J 56

Name _____ Date _____

 # Practice by Standard
Algebra and Functions 1.4

4AF1.4 Use and interpret formulas (e.g., area = length × width or $A = lw$) to answer questions about quantities and their relationships.

1 Which equation below represents the area (A) of the rectangle in square meters?

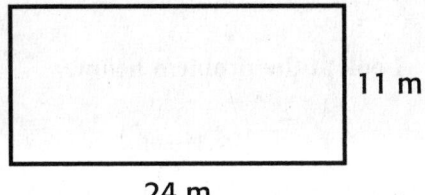

11 m

24 m

    A $24 = A \times 11$
    B $A = (2 \times 24) + (2 \times 11)$
    C $A = 24 \times 11$
    D $11 = (2 \times 24) + (2 \times A)$

2 A train travels 322 miles for 7 hours. Which equation represents the average number of miles (m) traveled by the train in one hour?

    F $322 = 7 \div m$
    G $m = 322 \times 7$
    H $322 = 7 \times m$
    J $7 = 322 \times m$

3 Rebecca needs to find the number of quarts (q) in 15 gallons. Which equation will help her? (4 quarts = 1 gallon)

    A $q = 4 \times 15$
    B $15 = 4 - q$
    C $q = \dfrac{15}{4}$
    D $q = (4 \times 1) + (4 \times 5)$

4 The perimeter (P) of the rectangle below is 110 yd. Which equation represents the value of x?

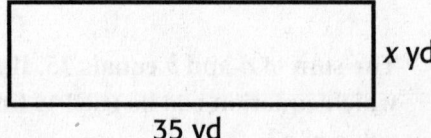

x yd

35 yd

    F $110 = (2 \times x) + 35$
    G $110 = (2 \times x) + (2 \times 35)$
    H $110 = 35 \times x$
    J $110 = x (2 \times 35)$

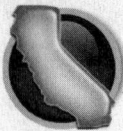

Practice by Standard
Algebra and Functions 1.5

4AF1.5 **Understand that an equation such as $y = 3x + 5$ is a prescription for determining a second number when a first number is given.**

1 Look at the problem below.

$$Y + D = 34$$

If $Y = 17$, what is D?

A 2
B 17
C 34
D 51

2 The sum of a and b equals 15. If $b = 5$, which equation can be used to find the value of a?

F $a + 15 = 5$
G $5 + 15 = a$
H $a + 5 = 15$
J $a - 15 = a$

3 Using the equation below, what is the value of y when x is 4?

$$y = 2x - 1$$

A 5
B 6
C 7
D 8

4 The difference between z and t equals 11. If $t = 2$, which equation can be used to find the value of z?

F $z + 2 = 11$
G $z - 2 = 11$
H $2 + 11 = z$
J $z + 11 = 2$

5 Look at the problem below.

$$\square \div V = 6$$

If $V = 4$, what is $\square$?

A 2
B 6
C 10
D 24

6 The product of h and k equals 28. If $k = 14$, which equation can be used to find the value of h?

F $h \times 14 = 28$
G $k \times 14 = 28$
H $h + 28 = k$
J $h - 14 = 28$

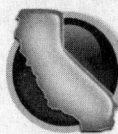

Practice by Standard
Algebra and Functions 2.1

4AF2.1 **Know and understand that equals added to equals are equal.**

1 The letters *r* and *s* stand for numbers. If $s + 30 = r + 30$, which statement is true?

A $r = s$
B $r > s$
C $r = s - 30$
D $r < s$

2 What goes in the ☐ to make this number sentence true?

$$45 + 3 = 45 + \boxed{}$$

F $1 + 1$
G $1 + 2$
H $3 + 2$
J 6

3 The letters *k* and *h* stand for numbers. If $k + 20 = h + 30$, which statement is true?

A $k - h < 10$
B $k - h = 10$
C $k - h > 10$
D $k - h = 20$

4 What is the value of *w*?

$$w + 9 = 33 + 9$$

F 9
G 24
H 33
J 42

5 The letters *g* and *f* stand for numbers. If $f - 300 = g$, which statement is true?

A $f < g$
B $f = g$
C $f > g$
D f is not related to g

6 Which statement is true?

F $7 + (4 - 1) = 7 + \dfrac{3}{3}$

G $7 + (4 - 1) = 7 + \dfrac{6}{4}$

H $7 + (4 - 1) = 7 + \dfrac{12}{4}$

J $7 + (4 - 1) = 7 + \dfrac{16}{4}$

Practice by Standard
Algebra and Functions 2.1 (continued)

7 Which expression goes in the ☐ to make this number sentence true?

$$8 + (2 + 3) = \boxed{} + 5$$

A $2 + 1$
B $3 + 2$
C $5 + 3$
D $8 + 4$

8 $(9 \div 3) + 11 =$

F $1 + 11$
G $3 + 11$
H $4 + 11$
J $5 + 11$

9 What is the value of d?

$$7 + 5 = d + 5$$

A $4 - 3$
B $4 \div 3$
C $4 + 3$
D $4 - 3$

10 The letters A and B stand for numbers. If $A - 10 = B - 20$, which statement is true?

F $A < B$
G $A = B$
H $A > B$
J $A = B + 20$

11 Which expression is equivalent to the expression below?

$$(7 \times 11) - 14$$

A $18 - 4$
B $77 - 14$
C $(7 \times 11) - 2$
D 7×11

12 Which statement is true?

F $\dfrac{20}{5} + (3 \times 5) = 3 + 15$

G $\dfrac{15}{5} + (2 \times 5) = 3 + (15 + 5)$

H $\dfrac{30}{5} + (2 \times 3) = 6 + 5$

J $\dfrac{35}{5} + (4 \times 5) = 7 + 20$

13 The letters Y and Z stand for numbers. If $Y + 40 = Z$, which statement is true?

A $Z < Y$
B $Z = Y$
C $Y + 40 - 10 = Z - 10$
D $Y + 40 + 10 = Z - 10$

Name _____ Date _____

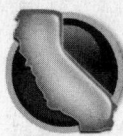

Practice by Standard
Algebra and Functions 2.2

4AF2.2 **Know and understand that equals multiplied by equals are equal.**

1 The letters w and x stand for numbers. If $w \times 12 = x \times 12$, which statement is true?

  A $w < x$
  B $w > x$
  C $w = x - 10$
  D $w = x$

2 What number goes in the ☐ to make this number sentence true?

$$(20 - 3) \times 3 = 17 \times \square$$

  F 0
  G 1
  H 2
  J 3

3 The letters c and d stand for numbers. If $c \times \frac{4}{5} = 2d \times \frac{4}{5}$, which statement is true?

  A $c = d$

  B $c = 2d$

  C $c = \frac{1}{2}d$

  D $c = \frac{4}{5}d$

4 What is the value of f?

$$f \times 9 = (4 \times 3) \times 9$$

  F 2×2
  G 2×3
  H 2×6
  J 2×8

5 The letters h and j stand for numbers. If h and j are equal, which statement is true?

  A $\frac{3}{12}h = \frac{4}{16}j$

  B $2h = \frac{5}{2}j$

  C $\frac{3}{4}h = \frac{7}{7}j$

  D $h \times 6 = j \times (2 \times 4)$

6 Which statement is true?

  F $9 \times (6 - 1) = 9 \times \frac{20}{4}$

  G $9 \times (6 - 1) = 9 \times 7$

  H $9 \times (6 - 1) = 9 \times \frac{24}{4}$

  J $9 \times (5 - 1) = 9 \times \frac{20}{4}$

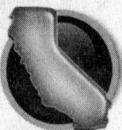

Practice by Standard
Algebra and Functions 2.2 (continued)

---

7 Which expression goes in the ☐ to make this number sentence true?

$$11 \times (3 + 3) = \boxed{} \times 6$$

A 4 + 5
B 4 + 6
C 4 + 7
D 4 + 8

---

8 $(3 \times 2) \times 7 =$

F 1×7
G 5×7
H 6×7
J 9×7

---

9 What is the value of *V*?

$$9 \times 3 = V \times 3$$

A 3 + 3
B 3 × 3
C 4 × 3
D 4 × 4

---

10 The letters *A* and *B* stand for numbers. If $A \times 12 = B \times 12$, which statement is true?

F $\frac{1}{7}A = \frac{1}{7}B$

G $\frac{1}{5}A = 5B$

H $A > B + 10$

J $A = B \times 2$

---

11 Which expression is equivalent to the expression below?

$$(7 \times 7) \times 14$$

A 14
B 7×7
C 7×14
D 49×14

---

12 Which statement is true?

F $\frac{35}{7} \times (3 + 5) = 5 \times (3 + 5)$

G $\frac{15}{5} \times (2 + 5) = 5 \times 7$

H $\frac{30}{6} \times (2 + 3) = 5 \times 4$

J $\frac{36}{3} + (1 \times 5) = 12 + 6$

---

13 The letters *M* and *P* stand for numbers. If $M \times 25 = P \times 25$, which statement is true?

A $M \times 10 = P \times 10$
B $M \neq P$
C $M > P$
D $M \times 43 = P \times 42$

Practice by Standard
Measurement and Geometry 1.1

4MG1.1 Measure the area of rectangular shapes by using appropriate units, such as square centimeter (cm²), square meter (m²), square kilometer (km²), square inch (in²), square yard (yd²), or square mile (mi²).

1 Mr. Baron is measuring his rectangular patio. The length of the patio is 20 feet. The width of the patio is 12 feet. What is the area of Mr. Baron's patio?

    A 252 square feet

    B 240 square feet

    C 64 square feet

    D 32 square feet

---

2 What is the area of the square below?

3 cm

    F 3 cm²

    G 6 cm²

    H 9 cm²

    J 12 cm²

3 The total area of a rectangular national park is 65 square miles. The width of the park is 5 miles. How long is the park?

    A 5 miles

    B 13 miles

    C 18 miles

    D 60 miles

---

4 What is the area of the figure below?

6 feet

20 feet

    F 26 square feet

    G 52 square feet

    H 120 square feet

    J 180 square feet

---

5 Alisa wants to carpet the floor of her bedroom. The length of her room is 4 meters and the width is 6 meters. How much carpet will Alisa need?

    A 10 square meters

    B 20 square meters

    C 22 square meters

    D 24 square meters

Practice by Standard
Measurement and Geometry 1.2 and 1.3

4MG1.2 Recognize that rectangles that have the same area can have different perimeters.

1 Which statement about the figures is true?

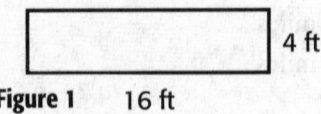

Figure 1 16 ft, 4 ft

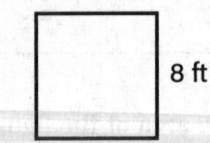

Figure 2 8 ft, 8 ft

A They both have the same perimeter.

B The perimeter of Figure 2 is greater than the perimeter of Figure 1.

C They both have the same area.

D They both have the same width.

2 Which two figures have the same perimeter?

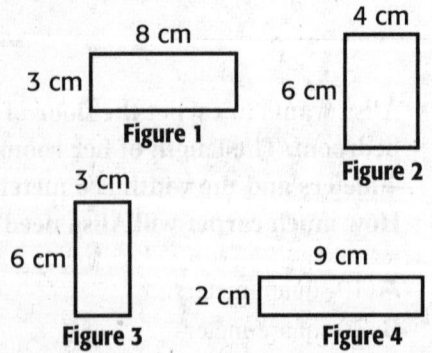

8 cm, 3 cm **Figure 1**

4 cm, 6 cm **Figure 2**

3 cm, 6 cm **Figure 3**

9 cm, 2 cm **Figure 4**

F Figure 1 and Figure 4

G Figure 2 and Figure 3

H Figure 1 and Figure 2

J Figure 3 and Figure 4

4MG1.3 Understand that rectangles that have the same perimeter can have different areas.

1 Which two figures have the same area?

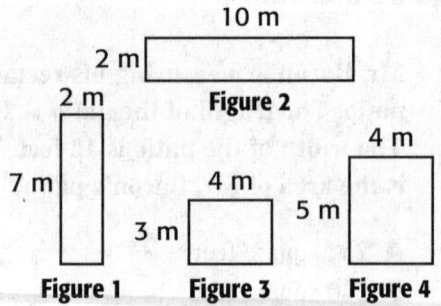

10 m, 2 m **Figure 2**

2 m, 7 m **Figure 1**

4 m, 3 m **Figure 3**

4 m, 5 m **Figure 4**

A Figure 2 and Figure 3

B Figure 1 and Figure 3

C Figure 2 and Figure 4

D Figure 1 and Figure 4

2 Which statement about the figures is not true?

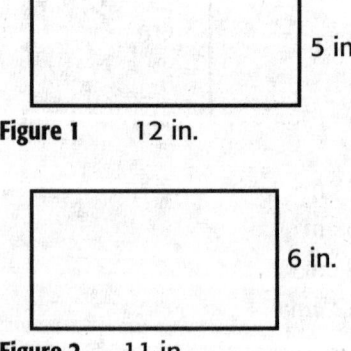

5 in. **Figure 1** 12 in.

6 in. **Figure 2** 11 in.

F They both have the same perimeter.

G The area of Figure 2 is greater than the area of Figure 1.

H The perimeter of Figure 1 is less than the perimeter of Figure 2.

Practice by Standard
Measurement and Geometry 1.4

4MG1.4 Understand and use formulas to solve problems involving perimeters and areas of rectangles and squares. Use those formulas to find the areas of more complex figures by dividing the figures into basic shapes.

1 The perimeter of square *A* is 48 in.

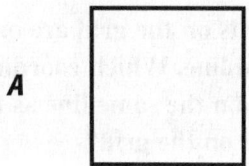

Kelly formed the new figure *B* as shown below. What is the perimeter of figure *B*?

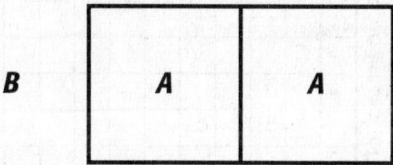

A 48 in.
B 72 in.
C 96 in.
D 108 in.

2 What is the perimeter of the figure below?

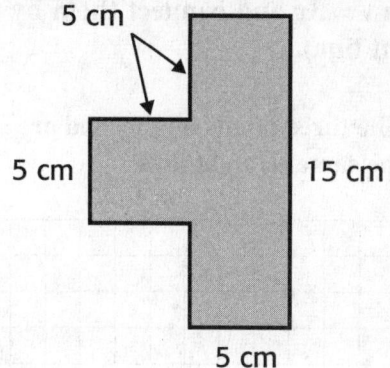

5 cm

5 cm   15 cm

5 cm

F 100 cm   **H** 50 cm
G 55 cm   **J** 35 cm

3 The area of the entire figure below is 372 m². What is the area of the shaded part of the figure?

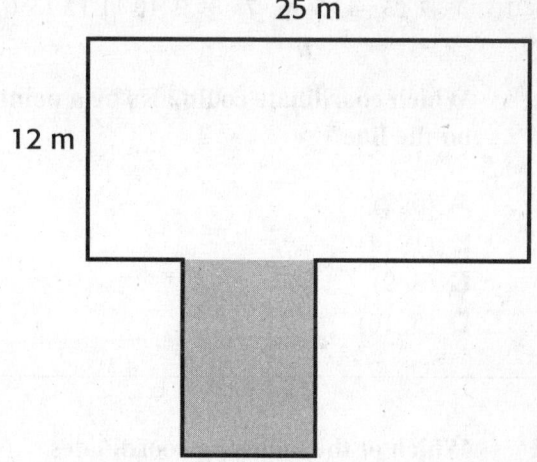

25 m

12 m

A 62 m²
B 72 m²
C 300 m²
D 372 m²

Practice by Standard
Measurement and Geometry 2.1

4MG2.1 Draw the points corresponding to linear relationships on graph paper (e.g., draw 10 points on the graph of the equation $y = 3x$ and connect them by using a straight line).

1 The three points on the grid are all on the same straight line.

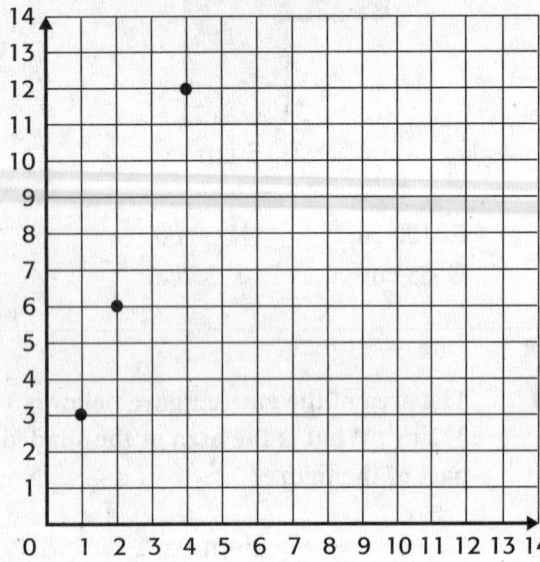

Which coordinate could also be a point on the line?

A (0, 2)

B (1, 14)

C (3, 9)

D (5, 16)

2 Which of the following coordinates could be on the same line as the set of coordinates (3, 1), (5, 3), and (8, 6)?

F (4, 2)   **H** (6, 8)

G (9, 8)   **J** (2, ⁻4)

3 Which set of coordinates could all be on the same straight line?

A (0, 0), (1,1), (2, 1)

B (2, 3), (2, 4), (2, 5)

C (0, 3), (1, 3), (3, 0)

D (2, 0), (0, 2), (1, 0)

4 The two points on the grid are on the same straight line. Which coordinates could not be on the same line as the points shown on the grid?

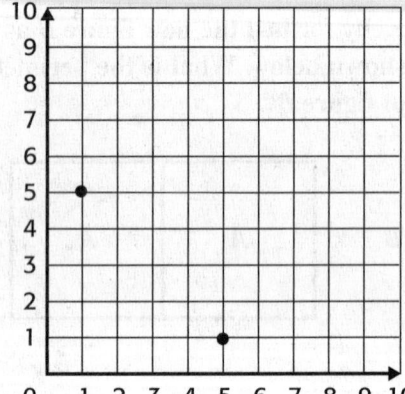

F (0, 6)

G (2, 4)

H (3, 4)

J (4, 2)

Practice by Standard
Measurement and Geometry 2.2

4MG2.2 Understand that the length of a horizontal line segment equals the difference of the *x*-coordinates.

1 What is the length of the line segment shown below?

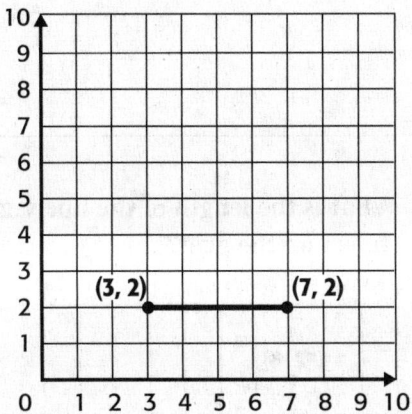

A 2 units
B 4 units
C 5 units
D 6 units

2 The point (5, 2) and point *C* are on the same horizontal line on a grid. The length of the line between the two points is 6 units. Which of the following could be the first coordinate of point *C*?

F 7
G 9
H 11
J 13

3 Which pair of coordinates could be on the same horizontal line?

A (0, 1), (1, 1)
B (5, 6), (5, 7)
C (1, 3), (1, 9)
D (4, 2), (11, 3)

4 Look at the graph. Point *K* is at (2, 5). Point *M* is at (9, 5).

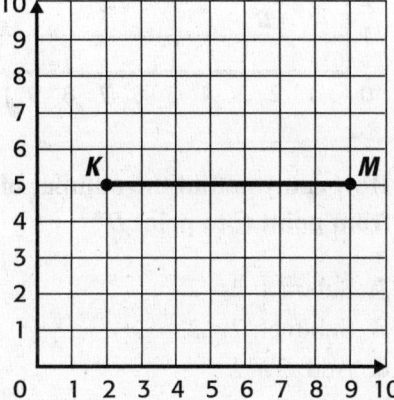

How can you find the number of units from point *K* to point *M*?

F Subtract: 5 − 5.
G Subtract: 9 − 2.
H Add: 2 + 5.
J Add: 2 + 9.

Practice by Standard
Measurement and Geometry 2.3

4MG2.3 Understand that the length of a vertical line segment equals the difference of the *y*-coordinates.

1 Look at the graph. Point *C* is at (2, 7). Point *D* is at (2, 2).

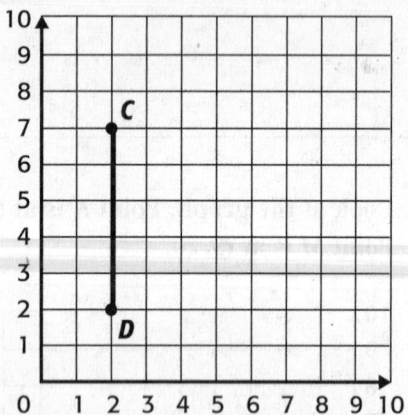

How can you find the number of units from point *C* to point *D*?

A Subtract: 2 – 2.

B Subtract: 7 – 2.

C Add: 2 + 2.

D Add: 7 + 2.

2 Which coordinate names a point that could be 4 units from the point (3, 7)?

F (3, 1)

G (3, 2)

H (3, 3)

J (3, 4)

3 Which coordinate names a point that could be 7 units from the point (⁻5, 4)?

A (⁻5, 2)

B (⁻5, 10)

C (⁻5, 11)

D (⁻5, 13)

4 What is the length of the line segment shown on the grid?

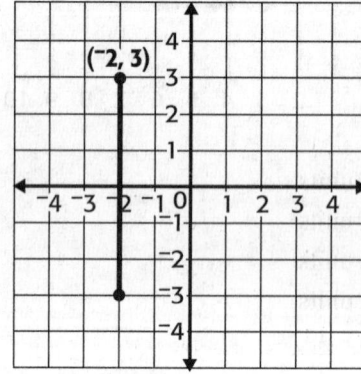

F 3 units

G 5 units

H 6 units

J 7 units

Practice by Standard
Measurement and Geometry 3.1

4MG3.1 **Identify lines that are parallel and perpendicular.**

1 Which figures below show pairs of lines that appear to be parallel?

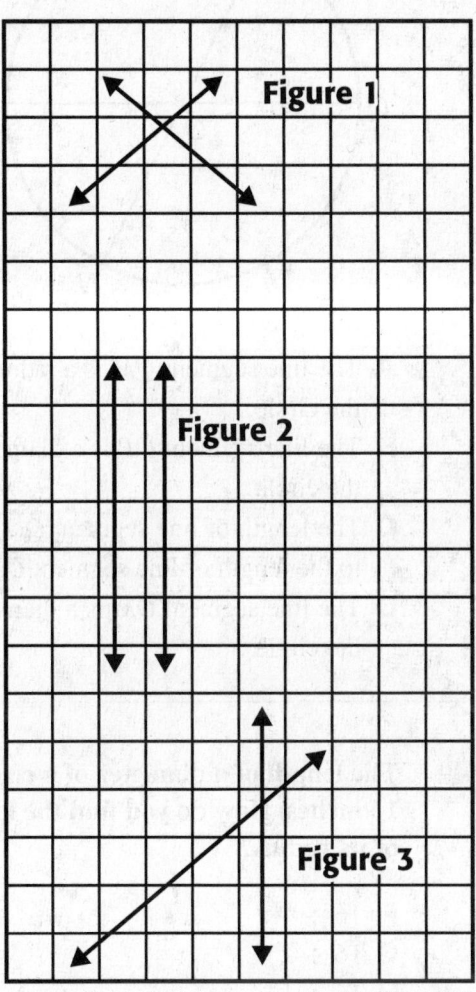

A Figure 1 and Figure 2
B Figure 2 and Figure 3
C Figure 1 only
D Figure 2 only

2 Which figures below show pairs of lines that appear to be perpendicular?

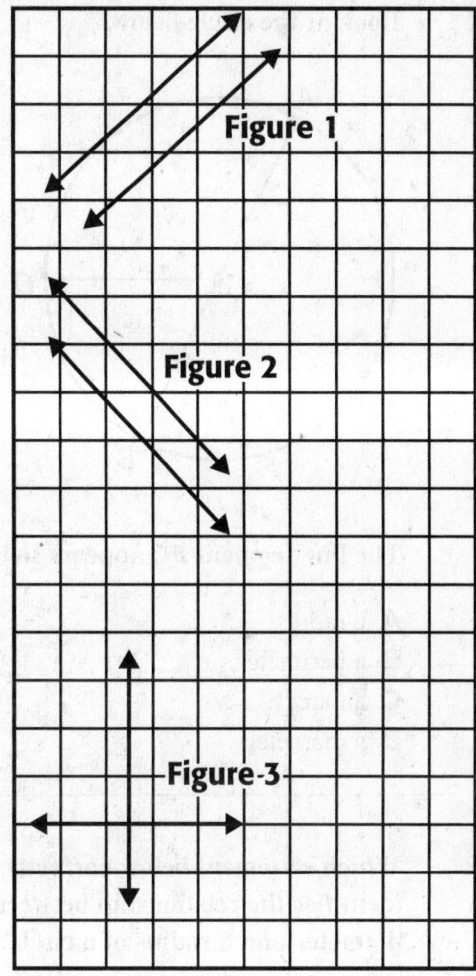

F Figure 1 and Figure 2
G Figure 1 only
H Figure 2 only
J Figure 3 only

Practice by Standard
Measurement and Geometry 3.2

4MG3.2 **Identify the radius and diameter of a circle.**

1 Look at the circle below.

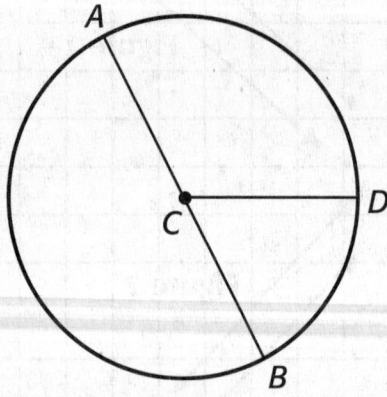

The line segment *BC* appears to be

A a radius.
B a perimeter.
C an arc.
D a diameter.

2 Which statement below correctly identifies the relationship between a diameter and a radius of a circle?

F The length of the radius is $\frac{1}{4}$ the length of the diameter.

G The length of the radius is $\frac{1}{2}$ the length of the diameter.

H The length of the radius is twice the length of the diameter.

J The radius is not related to the diameter.

3 Which statement is true about the circle shown below?

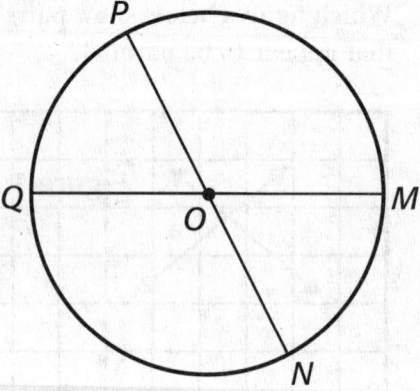

A The line segment *QM* is a radius of the circle.
B The line segment *OP* is a diameter of the circle.
C The length of line segment *QO* is equal to the length of line segment *ON*.
D The line segment *OM* is a diameter of the circle.

4 The length of a diameter of a circle is 16 inches. How do you find the length of its radius?

F $16 \div 4$
G $16 \div 2$
H $16 \div 1$
J 16×2

Practice by Standard
Measurement and Geometry 3.3 and 3.4

4MG3.3   Identify congruent figures.

1   Which pair of figures appear to be congruent?

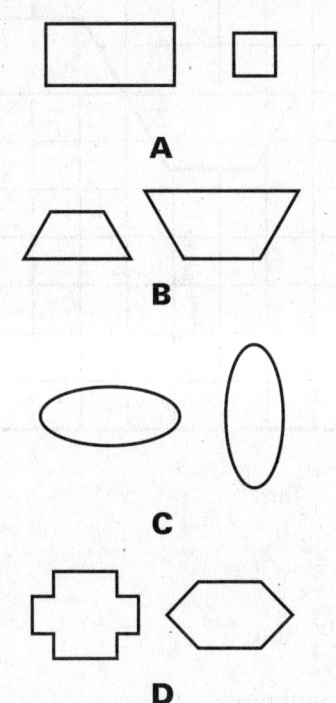

A

B

C

D

---

2   Which two figures below are congruent?

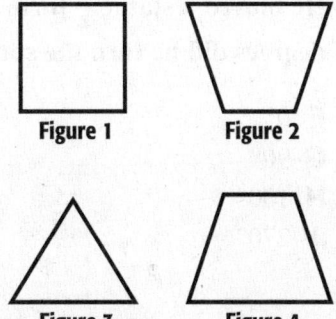

Figure 1   Figure 2

Figure 3   Figure 4

F Figure 1 and Figure 2
G Figure 1 and Figure 4
H Figure 2 and Figure 3
J Figure 2 and Figure 4

4MG3.4   Identify figures that have bilateral and rotational symmetry.

1   What type of symmetry does the figure shown below have?

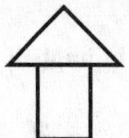

A rotational and bilateral symmetry
B only rotational symmetry
C only bilateral symmetry
D The figure does not have symmetry.

---

2   Which figure does not have rotational symmetry?

F
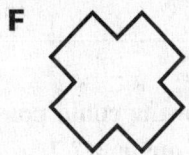

G
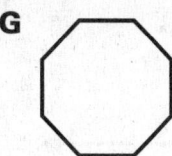

H
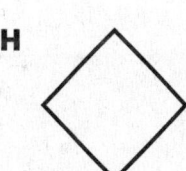

J

Practice by Standard
Measurement and Geometry 3.5

4MG3.5 Know the definitions of a right angle, an acute angle, and an obtuse angle. Understand that 90°, 180°, 270°, and 360° are associated, respectively, with $\frac{1}{4}$, $\frac{1}{2}$, $\frac{3}{4}$, and full turns.

1 What kind of angle is shown below?

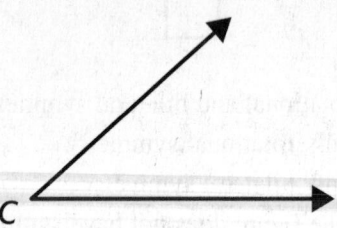

A an acute angle
B a right angle
C an obtuse angle
D a straight angle

2 Which of the following could possibly be the measure of angle *M*?

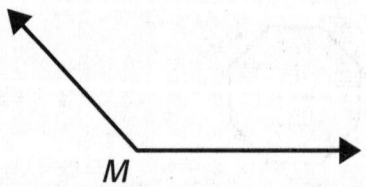

F 35°
G 135°
H 190°
J 370°

3 Which type of turn do the figures in the drawing show?

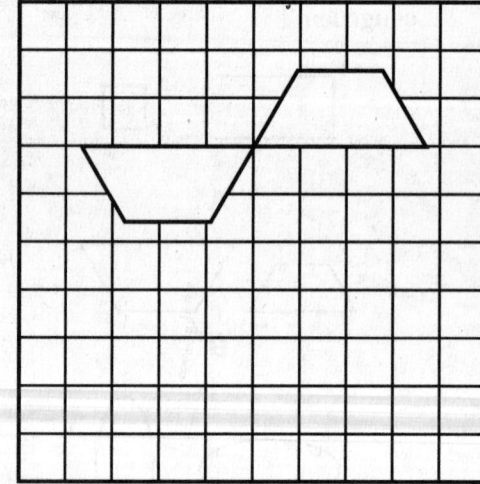

A $\frac{1}{4}$ turn

B $\frac{1}{2}$ turn

C $\frac{3}{4}$ turn

D Full turn

4 Mr. Romano works in an art museum. He moved a statue $\frac{1}{4}$ turn. How many degrees did he turn the statue?

F 0°
G 90°
H 180°
J 270°

 # Practice by Standard
Measurement and Geometry 3.6

4MG3.6 **Visualize, describe, and make models of geometric solids (e.g., prisms, pyramids) in terms of the number and shape of faces, edges, and vertices; interpret two-dimensional representations of three-dimensional objects; and draw patterns (of faces) for a solid that, when cut and folded, will make a model of the solid.**

1 Name the solid figure shown below.

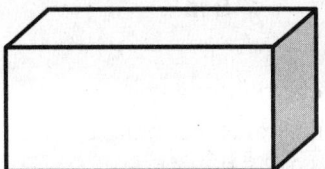

A rectangular prism
B triangular prism
C pyramid
D cylinder

2 Which of the following has six congruent square faces?

F rectangular prism
G square pyramid
H cylinder
J cube

3 Which of the following has two congruent triangular faces and three congruent rectangular faces?

A rectangular prism
B cylinder
C triangular prism
D triangular pyramid

4 Which solid figure can be formed when the figure below is folded on the dotted lines without overlapping?

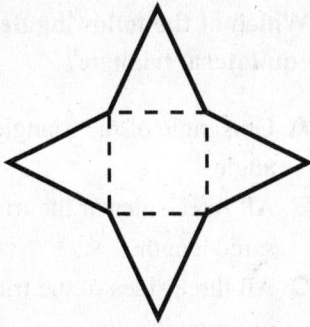

F cube
G rectangular prism
H square pyramid
J triangular prism

5 Name the solid figure shown below.

A triangular prism
B triangular pyramid
C square pyramid
D rectangular prism

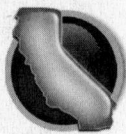

Practice by Standard
Measurement and Geometry 3.7

4MG3.7 **Know the definitions of different triangles (e.g., equilateral, isosceles, scalene) and identify their attributes.**

1 Which of the following describes an equilateral triangle?

A One angle of the triangle is an obtuse angle.

B All three sides of the triangle have the same length.

C All three sides of the triangle have different lengths.

D Only two sides of the triangle have the same length.

2 What type of triangle is shown below?

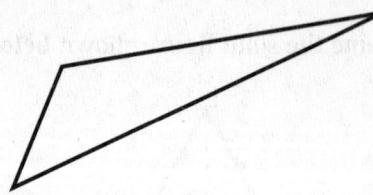

F isosceles triangle

G scalene triangle

H equilateral triangle

J right triangle

3 Which description best classifies the triangle shown below?

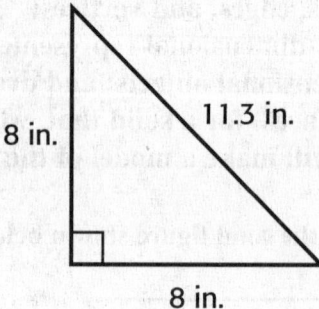

A scalene right triangle

B equilateral acute triangle

C isosceles right triangle

D scalene obtuse triangle

4 What is the name of a triangle that has one angle greater than 90°?

F acute triangle

G right triangle

H equilateral triangle

J obtuse triangle

Practice by Standard
Measurement and Geometry 3.8

4MG3.8 **Know the definition of different quadrilaterals (e.g., rhombus, square, rectangle, parallelogram, trapezoid).**

1 **What is the figure shown below?**

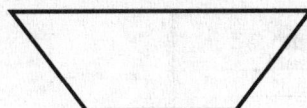

A rectangle
B trapezoid
C rhombus
D square

2 **Which statement is true?**

F A rhombus is also a parallelogram.
G A rectangle is a figure with four sides of equal length.
H A parallelogram has exactly one pair of parallel sides.
J A rectangle is also a square.

3 **Which of the following describes the figure shown below?**

A trapezoid
B rhombus
C rectangle
D square

4 **What is the sum of the angles of a rectangle?**

F 90°
G 180°
H 270°
J 360°

5 **What kind of quadrilateral *best* describes a baseball diamond?**

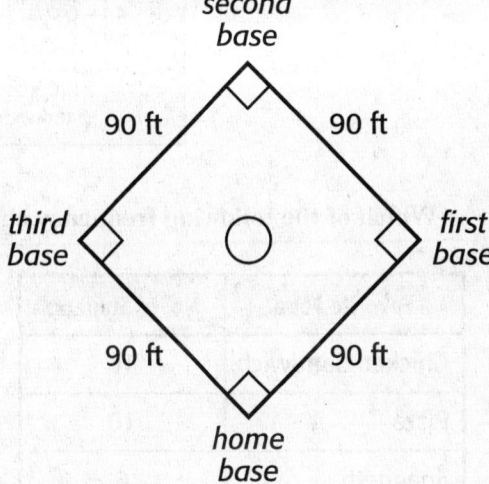

A square
B rhombus
C trapezoid
D rectangle

Practice by Standard
Statistics, Data Analysis, and Probability 1.1

4SDAP1.1 **Formulate survey questions; systematically collect and represent data on a number line; and coordinate graphs, tables, and charts.**

1 Kristina surveyed 45 students about their favorite lunch foods and then made this bar graph.

Which of the following frequency charts did she use to make this graph?

Favorite Food	No. of Students
Chicken Sandwich	16
Pizza	10
Spaghetti	6
Burrito	8

A

Favorite Food	No. of Students
Chicken Sandwich	15
Pizza	12
Spaghetti	8
Burrito	10

C

Favorite Food	No. of Students
Chicken Sandwich	16
Pizza	11
Spaghetti	8
Burrito	10

B

Favorite Food	No. of Students
Chicken Sandwich	16
Pizza	11
Spaghetti	10
Burrito	8

D

Name _____   Date _____

Practice by Standard
Statistics, Data Analysis, and Probability 1.2

4SDAP1.2 Identify the mode(s) for sets of categorical data and the mode(s), median, and any apparent outliers for numerical data sets.

1 What is the mode of this set of numbers?

$$\{3, 5, 5, 6, 6, 8, 8, 8, 10\}$$

A 5
B 6
C 8
D 10

2 Which set of numbers does not have a mode?

F {4, 4, 5, 7, 7, 15, 15, 15}
G {24, 25, 55, 77}
H {1, 5, 6, 6, 10, 10, 19}
J {100, 200, 200, 300, 300}

3 What is the median of this set of numbers?

$$\{25, 32, 10, 56, 32\}$$

A 10
B 25
C 30
D 32

4 Which of the following is not true about this set of data?

$$\{17, 17, 23, 25, 25, 35, 42, 42, 89\}$$

F The median of the data is 25.
G The set of data does not have a mode.
H There appears to be one outlier for this set of data.
J 17, 25, and 42 are the modes.

5 Which statement is true?

A Every set of numbers has at least one mode.
B An outlier is a number in a set of numbers that is not typical of that set.
C The median is the greatest number of a set of numbers.
D The mode is the middle number of a set of numbers.

6 What is the median of this set of numbers?

$$\{7, 7, 9, 12, 10, 6, 8\}$$

F 7
G 8
H 8.5
J 12

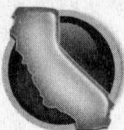

Practice by Standard
Statistics, Data Analysis, and Probability 1.3

4SDAP1.3 Interpret one- and two-variable data graphs to answer questions about a situation.

1 The double bar graph below shows the number of books read by grades 3 through 5 at Washington and Jefferson Elementary Schools. What is the difference between the total number of books read by each school?

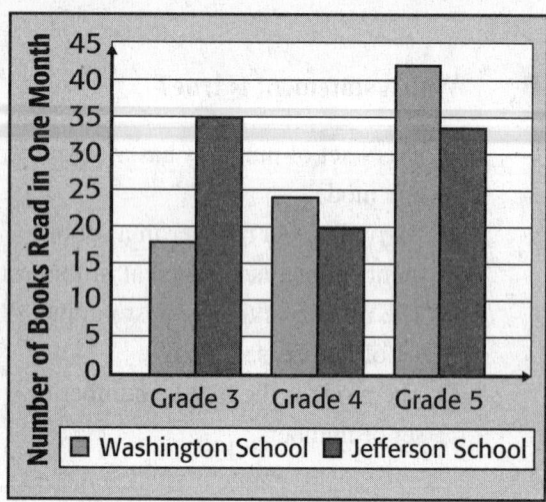

A 5
B 8
C 84
D 89

2 The graph below shows the number of miles Diana walked each day of a five-day hike. On which day did she walk the least distance?

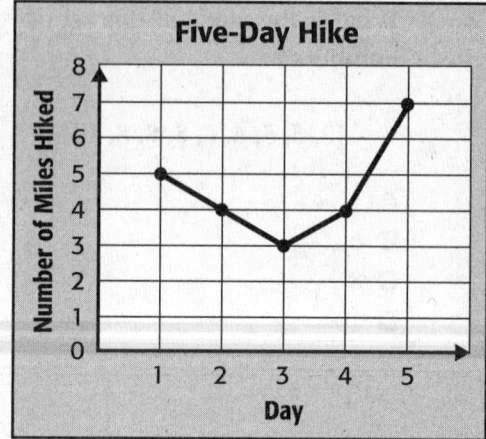

F Day 1
G Day 2
H Day 3
J Day 4

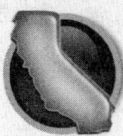

Practice by Standard
Statistics, Data Analysis, and Probability 2.1

4SDAP2.1 Represent all possible outcomes for a simple probability situation in an organized way (e.g., tables, grids, tree diagrams).

1 Matt rolls a six-sided number cube and then tosses a coin. Which tree diagram shows all the possible outcomes of his experiment?

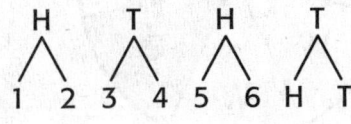

A

B

C

D

2 Manuel and Janet are eligible to be captain of their school debate team. James and Renee are eligible to be the co-captain. Each person has an equal chance of being chosen. Which set correctly shows all possible combinations of captain and co-captain?

F {Manuel – James, Manuel – Renee, Janet – James, Janet – Manuel}

G {Manuel – Janet, Manuel – Renee, Janet – James, Janet – Manuel}

H {Manuel – James, Manuel – Renee, Janet – James, Janet – Renee}

J {Renee – James, Manuel – Renee, Janet – Renee, Janet – Manuel}

3 Megan has a pair of black pants and a pair of brown pants. She also has a blue shirt, a yellow shirt, and a red shirt. How many different combinations of pants and shirts can Megan wear?

A 3
B 5
C 6
D 8

Practice by Standard
Statistics, Data Analysis, and Probability 2.2

4SDAP2.2 Express outcomes of experimental probability situations verbally and numerically (e.g., 3 out of 4; $\frac{3}{4}$).

1 A bag has 4 red marbles, 6 yellow marbles, 4 green marbles, and 2 blue marbles all the same size. Kyle pulls out 1 marble without looking. Which color is he least likely to choose?

A blue
B green
C yellow
D red

2 Mr. Hernandez writes each letter from the word UNITED on separate index cards. He puts the cards in a bag. A student draws one card out of the bag without looking. What is the probability that the student will pick a letter that is not T?

F 1 out of 6
G 3 out of 6
H 5 out of 6
J 6 out of 6

3 In the spinner below, G stands for Green and W stands for White. Maria spins the pointer once. What is the probability that she will land on white?

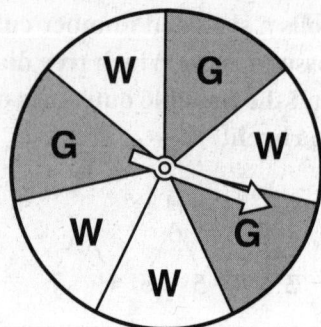

A $\frac{1}{7}$
B $\frac{2}{7}$
C $\frac{3}{7}$
D $\frac{4}{7}$

4 Robyn tosses a coin once. What is the probability that the coin will land on heads?

F $\frac{1}{8}$
G $\frac{1}{4}$
H $\frac{1}{2}$
J $\frac{3}{4}$

 # Standards Assessment
Student Answer Sheet

Record your answers by coloring in the appropriate bubble for the best answer to each question.

1 Ⓐ Ⓑ Ⓒ Ⓓ
2 Ⓕ Ⓖ Ⓗ Ⓙ
3 Ⓐ Ⓑ Ⓒ Ⓓ
4 Ⓕ Ⓖ Ⓗ Ⓙ
5 Ⓐ Ⓑ Ⓒ Ⓓ
6 Ⓕ Ⓖ Ⓗ Ⓙ
7 Ⓐ Ⓑ Ⓒ Ⓓ
8 Ⓕ Ⓖ Ⓗ Ⓙ
9 Ⓐ Ⓑ Ⓒ Ⓓ
10 Ⓕ Ⓖ Ⓗ Ⓙ
11 Ⓐ Ⓑ Ⓒ Ⓓ
12 Ⓕ Ⓖ Ⓗ Ⓙ
13 Ⓐ Ⓑ Ⓒ Ⓓ
14 Ⓕ Ⓖ Ⓗ Ⓙ
15 Ⓐ Ⓑ Ⓒ Ⓓ
16 Ⓕ Ⓖ Ⓗ Ⓙ
17 Ⓐ Ⓑ Ⓒ Ⓓ
18 Ⓕ Ⓖ Ⓗ Ⓙ
19 Ⓐ Ⓑ Ⓒ Ⓓ
20 Ⓕ Ⓖ Ⓗ Ⓙ
21 Ⓐ Ⓑ Ⓒ Ⓓ
22 Ⓕ Ⓖ Ⓗ Ⓙ

23 Ⓐ Ⓑ Ⓒ Ⓓ
24 Ⓕ Ⓖ Ⓗ Ⓙ
25 Ⓐ Ⓑ Ⓒ Ⓓ
26 Ⓕ Ⓖ Ⓗ Ⓙ
27 Ⓐ Ⓑ Ⓒ Ⓓ
28 Ⓕ Ⓖ Ⓗ Ⓙ
29 Ⓐ Ⓑ Ⓒ Ⓓ
30 Ⓕ Ⓖ Ⓗ Ⓙ
31 Ⓐ Ⓑ Ⓒ Ⓓ
32 Ⓕ Ⓖ Ⓗ Ⓙ
33 Ⓐ Ⓑ Ⓒ Ⓓ
34 Ⓕ Ⓖ Ⓗ Ⓙ
35 Ⓐ Ⓑ Ⓒ Ⓓ
36 Ⓕ Ⓖ Ⓗ Ⓙ
37 Ⓐ Ⓑ Ⓒ Ⓓ
38 Ⓕ Ⓖ Ⓗ Ⓙ
39 Ⓐ Ⓑ Ⓒ Ⓓ
40 Ⓕ Ⓖ Ⓗ Ⓙ
41 Ⓐ Ⓑ Ⓒ Ⓓ
42 Ⓕ Ⓖ Ⓗ Ⓙ
43 Ⓐ Ⓑ Ⓒ Ⓓ
44 Ⓕ Ⓖ Ⓗ Ⓙ

45 Ⓐ Ⓑ Ⓒ Ⓓ
46 Ⓕ Ⓖ Ⓗ Ⓙ
47 Ⓐ Ⓑ Ⓒ Ⓓ
48 Ⓕ Ⓖ Ⓗ Ⓙ
49 Ⓐ Ⓑ Ⓒ Ⓓ
50 Ⓕ Ⓖ Ⓗ Ⓙ
51 Ⓐ Ⓑ Ⓒ Ⓓ
52 Ⓕ Ⓖ Ⓗ Ⓙ
53 Ⓐ Ⓑ Ⓒ Ⓓ
54 Ⓕ Ⓖ Ⓗ Ⓙ
55 Ⓐ Ⓑ Ⓒ Ⓓ
56 Ⓕ Ⓖ Ⓗ Ⓙ
57 Ⓐ Ⓑ Ⓒ Ⓓ
58 Ⓕ Ⓖ Ⓗ Ⓙ
59 Ⓐ Ⓑ Ⓒ Ⓓ
60 Ⓕ Ⓖ Ⓗ Ⓙ
61 Ⓐ Ⓑ Ⓒ Ⓓ
62 Ⓕ Ⓖ Ⓗ Ⓙ
63 Ⓐ Ⓑ Ⓒ Ⓓ
64 Ⓕ Ⓖ Ⓗ Ⓙ
65 Ⓐ Ⓑ Ⓒ Ⓓ

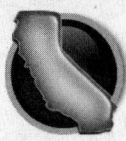

Standards Assessment

1 Look at the circle with center *S*.

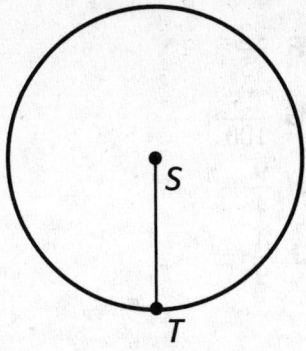

The line segment *ST* appears to be

A the center
B the diameter
C a chord
D the radius

2 Which of these is the number 918, 274?

F nine hundred eight thousand, two hundred seventy-four
G nine hundred eighteen, two hundred seventy-four
H nine hundred eighteen thousand, two seventy-four
J nine hundred eighteen thousand, two hundred seventy-four

3 $9{,}538 + 4{,}317 =$

A 5,221
B 5,241
C 13,845
D 13,855

4 Sandy solved the problem below. Which expression could be used to check her answer?

$$\overset{542r1}{4\overline{)2{,}169}}$$

F $(542 \times 4) + 1$
G $(542 \times 1) + 4$
H $(542 + 1) \times 4$
J $(542 + 4) \times 1$

5 What is the value of *p*?

$$p = (81 \div 3) + 9$$

A 37
B 36
C 18
D 9

Standards Assessment

6 Which of the following lists the mountain heights in order from tallest to shortest?

Mountain	Height (ft)
North Palisade	14,242
White Mt. Peak	14,246
Whitney	14,494
Williamson	14,375

F 14,494 > 14,375 > 14,246 > 14,242
G 14,242 > 14,246 > 14,494 > 14,375
H 14,494 > 14,375 > 14,242 > 14,246
J 14,242 > 14,246 > 14,375 > 14,494

7 What fraction is best represented by point C on this number line?

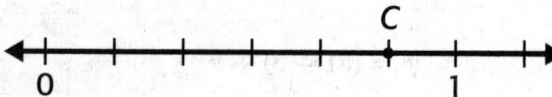

A $\frac{1}{6}$

B $\frac{5}{6}$

C $\frac{5}{7}$

D $\frac{6}{7}$

8 Which fraction means the same as 2.25?

F $2\frac{2}{5}$

G $\frac{25}{100}$

H $\frac{9}{4}$

J $\frac{4}{9}$

9 There are 60 art teachers in the Perryville School District. Each teacher is given 9,500 sheets of construction paper at the start of the year. How many sheets of construction paper is this in all?

A 5,700
B 57,000
C 570,000
D 5,700,000

10 What number equals 2,000,000 + 600,000 + 20,000 + 70?

F 26,270
G 2,620,070
H 26,200,070
J 262,000,070

Standards Assessment

11 Which statement about the figures is true?

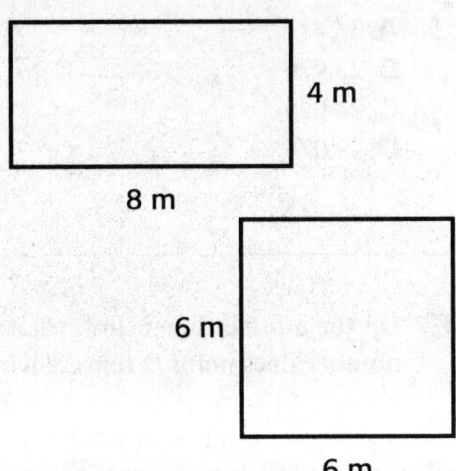

4 m

8 m

6 m

6 m

A They have the same perimeter.
B They have the same area.
C They have the same width.
D They are both squares.

12 What is the value of the expression below if $t = 3$?

$$t \times (5 + 0)$$

F 0
G 3
H 5
J 15

13 The line graph shows the estimated ticket sales at a stadium for the past five years.

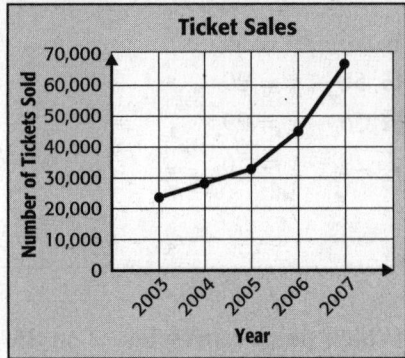

Which two years were ticket sales about the same?

A 2003 and 2004
B 2004 and 2005
C 2003 and 2005
D 2006 and 2007

14 $274 \div 6 =$

F 45
G 45 R4
H 46
J 46 R2

15 Which statement is true?

A The only factors of 7 are 1 and 7
B The only factors of 8 are 1 and 8
C The only factors of 9 are 1 and 9
D The only factors of 10 are 1 and 10

Standards Assessment

---

16 The difference of x minus y equals 29. If $x = 56$, which equation can be used to find the value of y?

F $x - 29 = 56$
G $56 - y = 29$
H $56 - x = 29$
J $29 - y = 56$

---

17 Which point represents ⁻3 on the number line below?

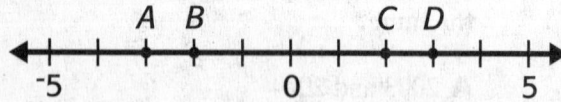

A A
B B
C C
D D

---

18 Lennie ran 150 miles in 5 days. He ran the same number of miles each day. How many miles did he run each day?

F 20
G 25
H 30
J 35

19
$$\begin{array}{r} 463 \\ \times\ 52 \\ \hline \end{array}$$

A 3,241
B 23,976
C 24,076
D 29,076

---

20 On the number line below, what number does point D represent?

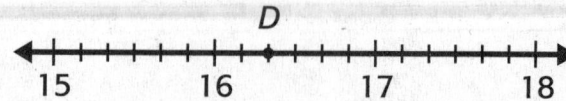

F $16\frac{1}{3}$

G $16\frac{2}{5}$

H $17\frac{1}{3}$

J $17\frac{2}{6}$

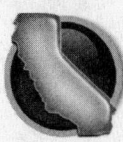

Standards Assessment

21 Find the value of the expression.

$$2 \times (6 + 4)$$

   A 12
   B 16
   C 20
   D 26

22 On a coordinate grid, Point A is at (3, 10) and Point C is at (7, 10). What is the length of the line segment that connects Point A to Point C?

   F 3 units
   G 4 units
   H 7 units
   J 10 units

23 On Thursday night, there were 212 people at the school musical. On Friday night, there were 267 people, and Saturday night there were 349 people. Approximately how many people attended the school musical in the three days?

   A 700 people
   B 800 people
   C 900 people
   D 1,000 people

24 What is the mode of this set of numbers?

$$3, 4, 5, 5, 6, 7, 9$$

   F 3
   G 4
   H 5
   J 6

25 The sum of x plus y equals 19. If $x = 12$, which equation can be used to find the value of y?

   A $19 = x - y$
   B $y = 19 + x$
   C $y + 12 = 19$
   D $19 = 12 + x$

26 There are 130 students in the fourth grade at Voltz Elementary. The students need to sit in 5 rows during an assembly. How many students will be in each row?

   F 25
   G 26
   H 30
   J 34

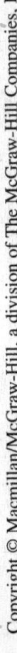

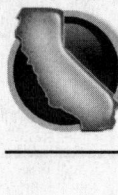

Standards Assessment

27 Sarah deposited $250 in her savings account. Then she took $75 out to buy new clothes. What number represents the money she spent?

A 175
B 75
C ⁻75
D ⁻175

---

28 $72,035 + 9,846 =$

F 71,871
G 71,881
H 81,871
J 81,881

---

29 The height of a skyscraper is 314.76 feet. What is the height of the skyscraper rounded to the nearest whole number?

A 300 feet
B 314 feet
C 315 feet
D 320 feet

30 Which equation below represents the area (*A*) of this rectangle in square inches?

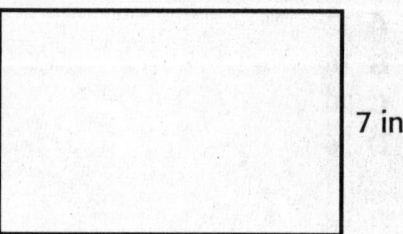

11 in.

F $A = (2 \times 11) + (2 \times 7)$
G $A = (2 + 11) \times (2 + 7)$
H $A = 2 \times (11 \times 7)$
J $A = 11 \times 7$

---

31 Which of the following has the greatest value?

A 3.00
B 3.20
C 3.02
D 2.03

32
$$20,659$$
$$- 16,231$$

F 3428
G 4428
H 5428
J 6428

Standards Assessment

33 Which is a prime number?

   A 3
   B 6
   C 12
   D 18

34 What number goes in the box to make this number sentence true?

$$(6 + 6) \times 2 = \square \times 6$$

   F 4
   G 5
   H 6
   J 12

35 Which number is represented by m?

$$3 \times m = 144$$

   A 40
   B 44
   C 48
   D 52

36 Josh graphed the equation $y = 3x$ on the coordinate plane shown. Which ordered pair below would work in the equation?

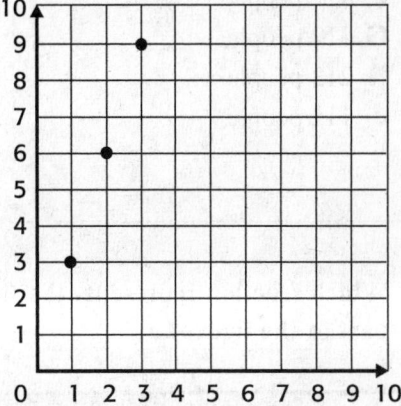

   F (0, 3)
   G (3, 1)
   H (4, 7)
   J (4, 12)

37 Ms. Payton bought 48 T-shirts. If each T-shirt cost \$12, how much money did Ms. Payton spend?

   A \$466
   B \$566
   C \$576
   D \$676

Standards Assessment

38 There are 24 groups of people touring a museum. There are 13 people in each group. How many people are touring the museum?

- **F** 412 people
- **G** 312 people
- **H** 212 people
- **J** 112 people

39 Which fraction represents the shaded part of the figure?

- **A** $\frac{3}{3}$
- **B** $\frac{2}{3}$
- **C** $\frac{1}{2}$
- **D** $\frac{3}{7}$

40 Find the value of the expression.

$$(9 + 5) \div (4 + 3)$$

- **F** 45
- **G** 38
- **H** 14
- **J** 2

41 Look at the graph. Point J is at (4, 8). Point K is at (4, 13).

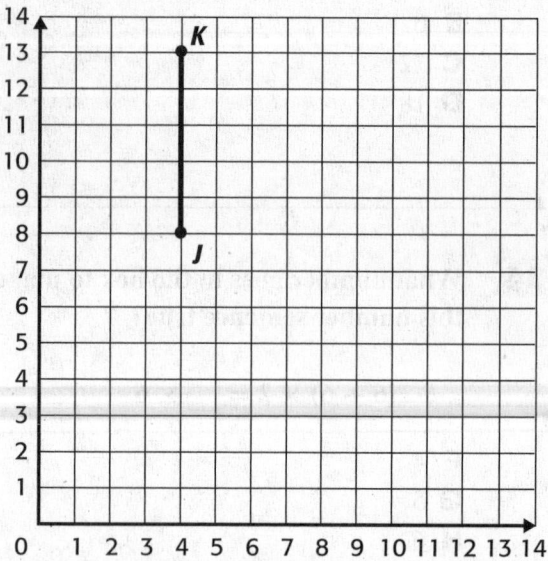

How can you find the number of units from point J to point K?

- **A** Add: $4 + 8$
- **B** Add: $8 + 13$
- **C** Subtract: $4 - 4$
- **D** Subtract: $13 - 8$

42 Ms. Kingery spent $693 on tickets to an amusement park. If she purchased 9 tickets, how much did each ticket cost?

- **F** $77
- **G** $79
- **H** $81
- **J** $87

Standards Assessment

43 What is the length of the line segment shown on the grid?

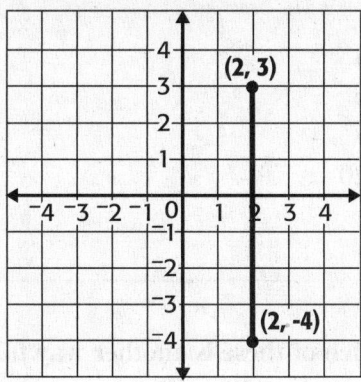

A 3 units

B 6 units

C 7 units

D 8 units

44 Find the value of the expression.

$$(2 \times 8) \times (3 + 3)$$

F 144

G 96

H 90

J 60

45 In 2005, the population of California was 33,871,648. What is this number rounded to the nearest hundred?

A 34,000,000

B 33,871,600

C 33,872,000

D 33,900,000

46 Joselynn's test scores are as follows 76, 98, 65, 80, 88, 79, 81. What is the median test score?

F 80

G 80.5

H 81

J 88

47 In which equation does $x = 3$?

A $x(10 - 3) = 21$

B $(2 \times 12) \div x = 3$

C $x - (1 \times 3) = 10$

D $(5 \times 5) + x = 30$

48 The letters W and V stand for numbers. If $W + 125 = V + 125$, which statement is true?

F $W > V$

G $W = V$

H $W < V$

J $W = V + 125$

Standards Assessment

49 What is the value of the expression below?

$$(4 \times 6) - (11 - 7)$$

A 14
B 20
C 24
D 28

50 What type of triangle is shown below?

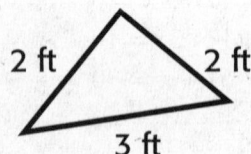

2 ft   2 ft
3 ft

F obtuse triangle
G equilateral triangle
H scalene triangle
J right triangle

51 A quadrilateral has one pair of parallel sides, two acute angles, and two obtuse angles. Name the quadrilateral described above.

A rectangle
B square
C parallelogram
D trapezoid

52 What is the value of r?

$$4 \times r = 6 \times (12 - 8)$$

F 4
G 6
H 8
J 20

53 Which of these is another way to write the product 18×5?

A $2 \times 7 \times 5$
B $2 \times 8 \times 5$
C $3 \times 9 \times 5$
D $6 \times 3 \times 5$

54 In 2005, thirty-two million, eight hundred two thousand, three hundred sixty-three passengers traveled through the San Francisco Airport. What is this number in standard form?

F 3,282,363
G 32,082,363
H 32,802,363
J 32,820,363

Standards Assessment

55 What is the value of the expression if $c = 6$?

$$(36 \div c) + (5 \times 10)$$

A 56
B 50
C 21
D 6

56 Look at the line segment shown below.

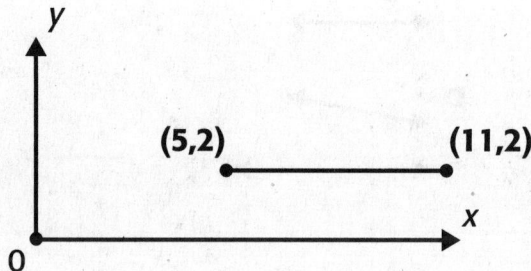

What is the length of the line segment?

F 2 units
G 5 units
H 6 units
J 16 units

57 Angle G is an obtuse angle. Which could be the measure of angle G?

A 180°
B 105°
C 90°
D 45°

58 Which expression goes in the box to make this number sentence true?

$$6 + 31 = \boxed{} + 31$$

F 4×2
G 2×2
H $4 + 2$
J $2 + 2$

59 What decimal is best represented by point H on this number line?

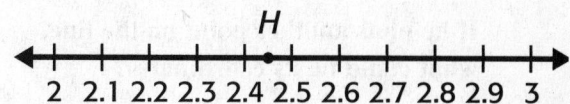

A 2.35
B 2.4
C 2.45
D 2.5

60 What is 5,822,790 rounded to the nearest hundred thousand?

F 5,800,000
G 5,820,000
H 5,900,000
J 6,000,000

Standards Assessment

61 Raul plotted 3 points on a grid. The 3 points were all on the same straight line.

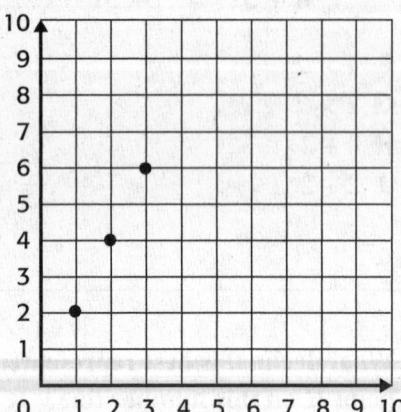

If he plots another point on the line, what could be its coordinates?

A (2, 1)
B (4, 2)
C (4, 8)
D (8, 4)

62 Look at the equation below.

$$(6 - 3) \times \triangle = \bigcirc \times (27 \div 9)$$

What is the relationship between $\triangle$ and $\bigcirc$?

F $\triangle > \bigcirc$
G $\triangle < \bigcirc$
H $\triangle = \bigcirc$
J $3 \times \triangle = \bigcirc$

63 Which pair of lines appear to be parallel?

A

B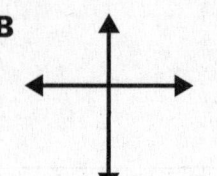

C

D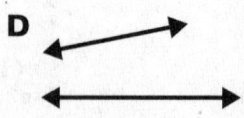

64 $22 + 5 = 22 + \square$

F $2 + 2$
G $3 + 3$
H $5 + 0$
J 22

 # Standards Assessment

65 Dulaney surveyed 35 students about their favorite after school activities and made this tally table to show the results.

Favorite After School Activities	
Watch t.v.	ⵑⵑ ⵑⵑ I
Play video games	ⵑⵑ IIII
Ride bikes	IIII
Take a nap	ⵑⵑ I
Read a book	ⵑⵑ

Which of the following bar graphs show the results of Dulaney's survey?

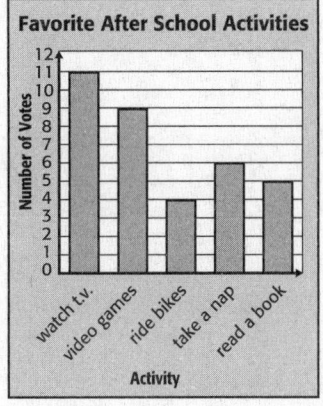

A

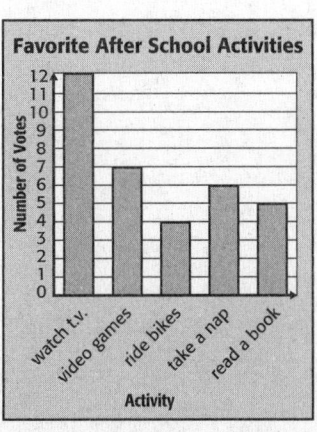

B

C

D

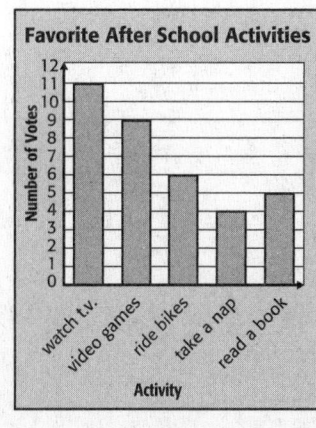

Workspace

Macmillan McGraw-Hill

California Mathematics 4

Standards Practice and Periodic Assessments

Mc Graw Hill **Macmillan McGraw-Hill**

The McGraw·Hill Companies

Mc Graw Hill ■ Macmillan McGraw-Hill

Copyright © by the McGraw-Hill Companies, Inc. All rights reserved. Except as permitted under the United States Copyright Act, no part of this publication may be reproduced or distributed in any form or by any means, or stored in a database or retrieval system, without prior permission of the publisher.

Send all inquiries to:
Macmillan/McGraw-Hill
8787 Orion Place
Columbus, OH 43240-4027

ISBN: 978-0-02-106356-7
MHID: 0-02-106356-7

Mastering the California Mathematics Standards, Grade 4
(Standards Practice and Periodic Assessments)

Printed in the United States of America

9 10 HES 15 14 13 12 11 10

Contents

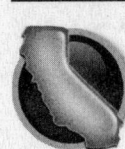# California Mathematics Standards, Grade 4

━● = key standard

Number Sense

1.0 Students understand the place value of whole numbers and decimals to two decimal places and how whole numbers and decimals relate to simple fractions. Students use the concepts of negative numbers:

━● 1.1 Read and write whole numbers in the millions.

━● 1.2 Order and compare whole numbers and decimals to two decimal places.

━● 1.3 Round whole numbers through the millions to the nearest ten, hundred, thousand, ten thousand, or hundred thousand.

━● 1.4 Decide when a rounded solution is called for and explain why such a solution may be appropriate. *Not assessable in multiple-choice format on the Grade 4 CST.*

1.5 Explain different interpretations of fractions, for example, parts of a whole, parts of a set, and division of whole numbers by whole numbers; explain equivalents of fractions (see Standard 4.0).

1.6 Write tenths and hundredths in decimal and fraction notations and know the fraction and decimal equivalents for halves and fourths (e.g., $\frac{1}{2} = 0.5$ or .50; $\frac{7}{4} = 1\frac{3}{4} = 1.75$).

1.7 Write the fraction represented by a drawing of parts of a figure; represent a given fraction by using drawings; and relate a fraction to a simple decimal on a number line.

━● 1.8 Use concepts of negative numbers (e.g., on a number line, in counting, in temperature, in "owing").

━● 1.9 Identify on a number line the relative position of positive fractions, positive mixed numbers, and positive decimals to two decimal places.

2.0 Students extend their use and understanding of whole numbers to the addition and subtraction of simple decimals:

2.1 Estimate and compute the sum or difference of whole numbers and positive decimals to two places.

2.2 Round two-place decimals to one decimal or the nearest whole number and judge the reasonableness of the rounded answer.

━● **3.0 Students solve problems involving addition, subtraction, multiplication, and division of whole numbers and understand the relationships among the operations:**

━● 3.1 Demonstrate an understanding of, and the ability to use, standard algorithms for the addition and subtraction of multidigit numbers.

 # California Mathematics Standards, Grade 4

◆— = key standard

Number Sense (continued)

◆—3.2 Demonstrate an understanding of, and the ability to use, standard algorithms for multiplying a multidigit number by a two-digit number and for dividing a multidigit number by a one-digit number; use relationships between them to simplify computations and to check results.

◆—3.3 Solve problems involving multiplication of multidigit numbers by two-digit numbers.

◆—3.4 Solve problems involving division of multidigit numbers by one-digit numbers.

4.0 Students know how to factor small whole numbers:

4.1 Understand that many whole numbers break down in different ways (e.g., $12 = 4 \times 3 = 2 \times 6 = 2 \times 2 \times 3$).

◆—4.2 Know that numbers such as 2, 3, 5, 7, and 11 do not have any factors except 1 and themselves and that such numbers are called prime numbers.

Algebra and Functions

1.0 Students use and interpret variables, mathematical symbols, and properties to write and simplify expressions and sentences:

1.1 Use letters, boxes, or other symbols to stand for any number in simple expressions or equations (e.g., demonstrate an understanding and the use of the concept of a variable).

◆—1.2 Interpret and evaluate mathematical expressions that now use parentheses.

◆—1.3 Use parentheses to indicate which operation to perform first when writing expressions containing more than two terms and different operations.

1.4 Use and interpret formulas (e.g., area = length × width or $A = lw$) to answer questions about quantities and their relationships.

◆—1.5 Understand that an equation such as $y = 3x + 5$ is a prescription for determining a second number when a first number is given.

◆—2.0 Students know how to manipulate equations:

◆—2.1 Know and understand that equals added to equals are equal.

◆—2.2 Know and understand that equals multiplied by equals are equal.

California Mathematics Standards, Grade 4

◆— = key standard

Measurement and Geometry

1.0 Students understand perimeter and area:

1.1 Measure the area of rectangular shapes by using appropriate units, such as square centimeter (cm^2), square meter (m^2), square kilometer (km^2), square inch (in^2), square yard (yd^2), or square mile (mi^2).

1.2 Recognize that rectangles that have the same area can have different perimeters

1.3 Understand that rectangles that have the same perimeter can have different areas.

1.4 Understand and use formulas to solve problems involving perimeters and areas of rectangles and squares. Use those formulas to find the areas of more complex figures by dividing the figures into basic shapes.

2.0 Students use two-dimensional coordinate grids to represent points and graph lines and simple figures:

◆—2.1 Draw the points corresponding to linear relationships on graph paper (e.g., draw 10 points on the graph of the equation $y = 3x$ and connect them by using a straight line).

◆—2.2 Understand that the length of a horizontal line segment equals the difference of the x- coordinates.

◆—2.3 Understand that the length of a vertical line segment equals the difference of the y- coordinates.

3.0 Students demonstrate an understanding of plane and solid geometric objects and use this knowledge to show relationships and solve problems:

3.1 Identify lines that are parallel and perpendicular.

3.2 Identify the radius and diameter of a circle.

3.3 Identify congruent figures.

3.4 Identify figures that have bilateral and rotational symmetry.

3.5 Know the definitions of a right angle, an acute angle, and an obtuse angle. Understand that 90°, 180°, 270°, and 360° are associated, respectively, with $\frac{1}{4}, \frac{1}{2}, \frac{3}{4}$, and full turns.

3.6 Visualize, describe, and make models of geometric solids (e.g., prisms, pyramids) in terms of the number and shape of faces, edges, and vertices; interpret two-dimensional representations of three-dimensional objects; and draw patterns (of faces) for a solid that, when cut and folded, will make a model of the solid.

 # California Mathematics Standards, Grade 4

= key standard

3.7 Know the definitions of different triangles (e.g., equilateral, isosceles, scalene) and identify their attributes.

3.8 Know the definition of different quadrilaterals (e.g., rhombus, square, rectangle, parallelogram, trapezoid).

Statistics, Data Analysis, and Probability

1.0 Students organize, represent, and interpret numerical and categorical data and clearly communicate their findings:

1.1 Formulate survey questions; systematically collect and represent data on a number line; and coordinate graphs, tables, and charts.

1.2 Identify the mode(s) for sets of categorical data and the mode(s), median, and any apparent outliers for numerical data sets.

1.3 Interpret one-and two-variable data graphs to answer questions about a situation.

2.0 Students make predictions for simple probability situations:

2.1 Represent all possible outcomes for a simple probability situation in an organized way (e.g., tables, grids, tree diagrams).

2.2 Express outcomes of experimental probability situations verbally and numerically (e.g., 3 out of 4; $\frac{3}{4}$).

Mathematical Reasoning

1.0 Students make decisions about how to approach problems:

1.1 Analyze problems by identifying relationships, distinguishing relevant from irrelevant information, sequencing and prioritizing information, and observing patterns.

1.2 Determine when and how to break a problem into simpler parts.

2.0 Students use strategies, skills, and concepts in finding solutions:

2.1 Use estimation to verify the reasonableness of calculated results.

2.2 Apply strategies and results from simpler problems to more complex problems.

2.3 Use a variety of methods, such as words, numbers, symbols, charts, graphs, tables, diagrams, and models, to explain mathematical reasoning.

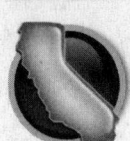

California Mathematics Standards, Grade 4

= key standard

Mathematical Reasoning (continued)

2.4 Express the solution clearly and logically by using the appropriate mathematical notation and terms and clear language; support solutions with evidence in both verbal and symbolic work.

2.5 Indicate the relative advantages of exact and approximate solutions to problems and give answers to a specified degree of accuracy.

2.6 Make precise calculations and check the validity of the results from the context of the problem.

3.0 Students move beyond a particular problem by generalizing to other situations:

3.1 Evaluate the reasonableness of the solution in the context of the original situation.

3.2 Note the method of deriving the solution and demonstrate a conceptual understanding of the derivation by solving similar problems.

3.3 Develop generalizations of the results obtained and apply them in other circumstances.

All Mathematical Reasoning standards are embedded in the questions on the Grade 4 CST.

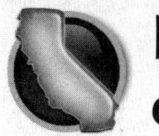

Practice by Chapter
Chapter 1 Place Value and Number Sense

1 A writer sold two million, fifty-three thousand, nine hundred eight copies of her book. What is this number in standard form?

A 2,053,908
B 2,053,980
C 2,530,908
D 2,530,980

2 Which of these is the number 5,420,078?

F five million, four hundred twenty, seven hundred eight
G five million, four hundred twenty thousand, seventy-eight
H five hundred forty-two thousand, seventy-eight
J five million, forty-two thousand, seventy-eight

3 What is the place value of the 8 in 382,615?

A hundreds
B thousands
C ten thousands
D hundred thousands

4 The estimated number of books in the Library of Congress is twenty-nine million. What is this number in standard form?

F 29,000
G 2,900,000
H 20,900,000
J 29,000,000

5 Which of the following has the greatest value?

A 1,312,400
B 1,006,562
C 1,282,573
D 1,324,311

6 Which is true?

F 4,033,317 > 4,330,201
G 782,511 > 4,330,201
H 4,033,201 = 4,330,201
J 4,033,317 < 4,330,201

7 What is 683,721 rounded to the nearest hundred-thousand?

A 600,000
B 680,000
C 684,000
D 700,000

Name _____ Date _____

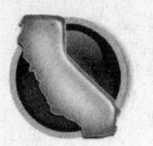
Practice by Chapter
Chapter 1 (continued)

8 The table below shows the areas of four states.

State	Area (sq. miles)
Arizona	113,998
Montana	147,042
California	163,696
New Mexico	121,589

What is the order of these states from smallest area to largest area?

F Arizona, Montana, California, New Mexico

G California, Montana, New Mexico, Arizona

H Montana, New Mexico, California, Arizona

J Arizona, New Mexico, Montana, California

9 Which of the following has the greatest value?

A 6,321,813
B 6,098,212
C 6,436,999
D 6,289,813

10 Sam has collected 213 stamps. He gave 57 stamps to his friend. How many stamps does Sam have now?

F 156
G 166
H 266
J 270

11 Riley wants a new bike that costs $125. She has saved $47. How much more money does Riley need to buy the bike?

A $172
B $122
C $88
D $78

12 Wendy is reading a 72-page book. If she reads 8 pages a day, how many days will it take her to read the entire book?

F 8 days
G 9 days
H 64 days
J 80 days

13 What is 36,492,817 rounded to the nearest hundred thousand?

A 36,500,000
B 36,000,000
C 37,000,000
D 40,000,000

Practice by Chapter
Chapter 2 Addition and Subtraction

1 $15 + 8 = 8 + \square$

     A 7
     B 8
     C 15
     D 23

2   The table below shows carnival attendance over a weekend.

Day	Attendance
Friday	478
Saturday	512
Sunday	453

Approximately how many people attended the carnival over the weekend?

     F 1,200 people
     G 1,300 people
     H 1,400 people
     J 1,500 people

3   Estimate.

$$45,782 + 3,241$$

     A 43,000
     B 48,000
     C 49,000
     D 76,000

4 $48,716 + 12,304 =$

     F 36,412
     G 50,010
     H 51,020
     J 61,020

5 $9,425 + 1,802$

     A 1,227
     B 7,623
     C 10,227
     D 11,227

6 $5,782 - 236$

     F 3,422
     G 5,546
     H 5,554
     J 5,556

7   There were 23,682 people cheering for the visiting team and 35,519 people cheering for the home team at a football game. How many people were cheering for a team at the game?

     A 58,191 people
     B 58,201 people
     C 59,191 people
     D 59,201 people

Practice by Chapter
Chapter 2 (continued)

8 46,214 − 13,238 =

   F 32,976
   G 33,024
   H 33,076
   J 33,086

9 The table shows the height of three mountain peaks in California. How much higher is Mount Whitney than Eagle Peak?

Mountain Peak	Height (feet)
Mount Whitney	14,491
Mount Shasta	14,162
Eagle Peak	9,892

   A 5,609 feet
   B 5,401 feet
   C 4,599 feet
   D 4,270 feet

10 There are 3,000 seats in a theater. If 1,862 people are sitting in the theater, how many seats are empty?

   F 1,138 seats
   G 2,248 seats
   H 2,862 seats
   J 4,862 seats

11
$$5,000$$
$$-\,2,607$$

   A 2,393
   B 2,403
   C 3,403
   D 3,607

12
$$30,600$$
$$-\,4,318$$

   F 34,918
   G 26,392
   H 26,292
   J 26,282

13 There were 13,352 people at the University basketball game. Of the people, 5,236 were students. How many people at the basketball game were *not* students?

   A 8,116
   B 8,124
   C 8,126
   D 18,588

Practice by Chapter
Chapter 3 Algebra: Use Addition and Subtraction

1 What is the value of the expression below if $y = 4$?

$$(15 + y) - (1 + 6)$$

- **A** 12
- **B** 16
- **C** 24
- **D** 26

2 Mindy is reading a 267-page book. She has 152 pages left to read. Which equation below can be used to find how many pages Mindy has read?

- **F** $267 + \square = 152$
- **G** $152 - 267 = \square$
- **H** $\square + 152 = 267$
- **J** $267 + 152 = \square$

3 Evaluate the expression below when $n = 5$.

$$20 - n$$

- **A** 4
- **B** 5
- **C** 15
- **D** 25

4 Which number is represented by b?

$$4 + b = 12$$

- **F** 3
- **G** 4
- **H** 8
- **J** 16

5 In which equation does $m = 6$?

- **A** $m - 5 = 11$
- **B** $3 + m = 19$
- **C** $10 + 4 = m$
- **D** $13 - m = 7$

6 Mike is 4 years younger than Jen. If Jen is y years old, which expression shows Mike's age?

- **F** $y + 4$
- **G** $y - 4$
- **H** $y = 4$
- **J** $4 - y$

7 The difference of x minus y equals 7. If $x = 24$, which equation can be used to find the value of y?

- **A** $24 - y = 7$
- **B** $24 + 7 = y$
- **C** $7 - y = 24$
- **D** $x - 7 = 24$

Practice by Chapter

Chapter 3 (continued)

8 Which of the following rules can be used for this function table?

a	b
3	9
7	13
15	21

F $b = 3 + a$

G $a = b + 6$

H $6 + a = b$

J $a + 8 = b$

9 The letters L and M each represent a number. If $L + 35 = M + 35$, which statement is true?

A $L = M$

B $L > M$

C $L < M$

D $L = M + 80$

10 Which expression goes in the box to make this number sentence true?

$$46 + 12 = \boxed{} + 46$$

F $1 + 2$

G $8 + 4$

H $6 - 6$

J $4 + 6$

11 Charlie bought a hat and a pair of gloves. The gloves cost $5 more than the hat. The gloves cost $9. How much did the hat cost?

A $4

B $5

C $14

D Not enough information is given.

12 There are 25 children on the playground. There are 5 more girls than boys. How many girls are on the playground?

F 30

G 20

H 15

J 10

13 In which equation does $b = 4$?

A $b + 3 = 8$

B $4 + b = 8$

C $10 - 4 = b$

D $10 + 6 = b$

Practice by Chapter
Chapter 4 Statistics: Data and Graphs

1 Kathy surveyed students about the number of pets they have. The line plot shows the results of her survey.

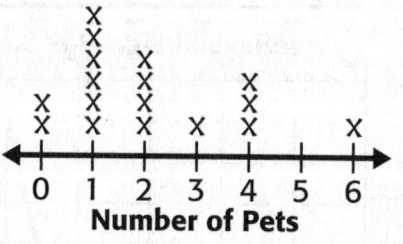

Number of Pets

How many students did Kathy survey?

A 7   **B** 15   **C** 17   **D** 21

2 What is the mode of the data in the line plot?

F 5   **G** 2   **H** 3   **J** 1

3 Reyes surveyed 30 students and made this bar graph.

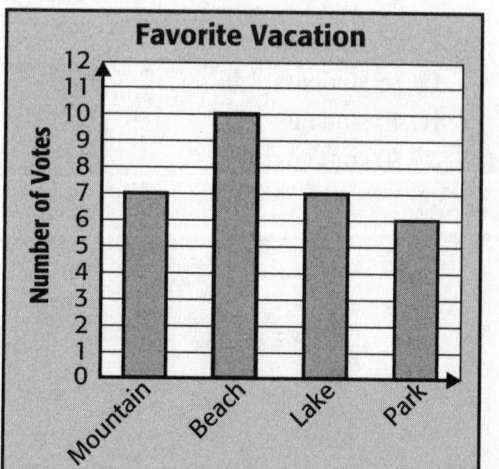

Which of the tally charts in the next column did he use to make this graph?

A

Favorite Vacation	
Mountain	
Beach	
Lake	ЖII
Park	I

B

Favorite Vacation	
Mountain	Ж III
Beach	Ж IIII
Lake	Ж I
Park	Ж II

C

Favorite Vacation	
Mountain	Ж III
Beach	Ж Ж I
Lake	Ж III
Park	Ж II

D

Favorite Vacation	
Mountain	Ж II
Beach	Ж Ж
Lake	Ж II
Park	Ж I

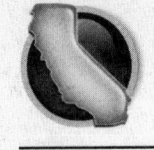

Practice by Chapter
Chapter 4 (continued)

4 What is the median of this set of numbers?

{1, 3, 5, 7, 8, 9, 9}

F 6
G 7
H 8
J 9

5 Pam and George signed up for a walking program. The bar graph shows the number of miles the students walked each week.

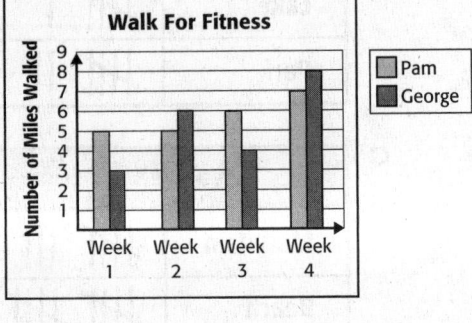

Walk For Fitness

How many total miles did George walk in the 4 weeks?

A 21 miles
B 23 miles
C 25 miles
D 44 miles

6 The line graph shows the number of students who signed up for the volleyball league each year.

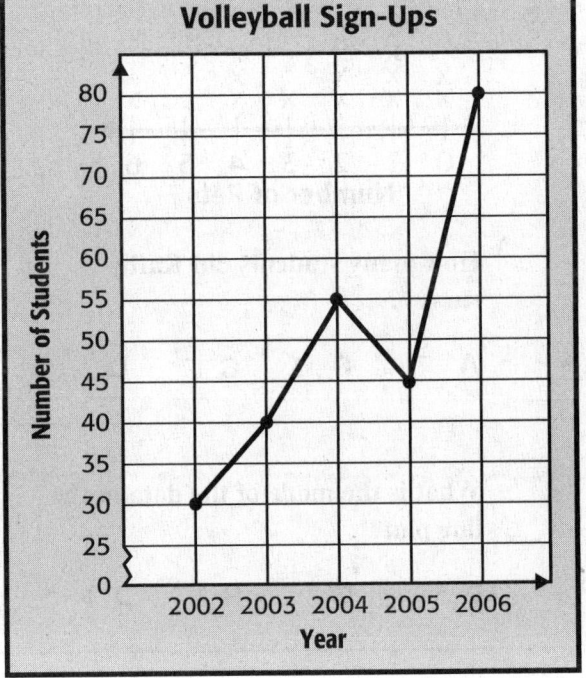

Volleyball Sign-Ups

How many more students signed up for volleyball in 2006 than in 2003?

F 25 students
G 35 students
H 40 students
J 50 students

Name _____   Date _____

Practice by Chapter
Chapter 5 Multiplication and Division Facts

1 Look at this multiplication sentence.

$$9 \times 4 = 36$$

Which division sentence is related to this multiplication sentence?

A $36 \div 6 = 6$
B $9 \div 3 = 3$
C $36 \div 9 = 4$
D $36 \div 3 = 12$

2 Which number can be multiplied by 683 to give the product 683?

$$683 \times \square = 683$$

F 0
G 1
H 2
J 10

3 Which multiplication expression has a product of 32?

A 8×4
B 3×9
C 7×5
D 6×6

4 $7\overline{)56}$

F 6
G 7
H 8
J 9

5 $12 \times 4 = \square$

A 3
B 16
C 42
D 48

6 Eddie collects stamps. He keeps his stamps in a 12 page book. There are 6 stamps on each page. Which number sentence shows how to find the number of stamps Eddie has?

F $12 + 6 = \square$

G $12 - 6 = \square$

H $12 \times 6 = \square$

J $12 \div 6 = \square$

7 There are 72 students in the fourth grade at Sunnydale Elementary School. The gym teacher separated the fourth graders into 8 equal groups for field day. How many students were in each group?

A 9
B 8
C 7
D 6

Practice by Chapter

Chapter 5 (continued)

8 Liz is organizing her books. She places 12 books on each shelf. There are 5 shelves. How many books does Liz have?

F 17

G 50

H 60

J 72

9 A store is having a sale on office supplies. Adam bought 4 packs of paper and an ink cartridge for his printer. The paper cost $6 a pack and the ink cartridge cost $28. How much did Adam spend altogether?

A $52

B $42

C $34

D $13

10 Carlos solved the problem below. Which expression could be used to check his answer?

$$6\overline{)54}^{\,9}$$

F $9 + 6$

G 6×9

H $54 \div (9 - 6)$

J $54 - (9 + 6)$

11 $5 \times 7 \times 2 = \square$

A 5×9

B 12×2

C 5×5

D 7×10

12 Which of these is another way to write the product 11×9?

F $11 \times 3 \times 3$

G $11 \times 5 \times 4$

H $11 \times 6 \times 3$

J $11 \times 7 \times 2$

13 Which is *not* a prime number?

A 2

B 7

C 9

D 11

14 Which of the following is equal to $12 \times 5 \times 2$?

F 12×7

G 17×2

H 12×10

J 12×2

Practice by Chapter
Chapter 6 Algebra: Use Multiplication and Division

1 What is the value of the expression below if $y = 5$?

$$(3 \times 4) + (2 \times y)$$

A 22

B 42

C 70

D 90

2 There are 64 crayons in the art room. The art teacher separates the crayons equally into boxes. She puts 8 crayons in each box. Which equation below can be used to find how many boxes the teacher used?

F $64 \div 8 = \square$

G $\square \div 8 = 64$

H $8 \times 64 = \square$

J $64 - 8 = \square$

3 Evaluate the expression below when $c = 4$.

$$12 \times c$$

A 3

B 8

C 16

D 48

4 Which number is represented by r?

$$r \div 3 = 24$$

F 6

G 8

H 27

J 72

5 $3 + (5 \times 4) - (9 \div 3) =$

A 7

B 8

C 20

D 29

6 $6 \times (7 - 3) =$

F 24

G 30

H 39

J 45

7 The product of a and b is 36. If $a = 4$, which equation can be used to find the value of b?

A $36 \div a = 4$

B $4 \times b = 36$

C $36 \times 4 = b$

D $b \div 4 = 36$

Practice by Chapter
Chapter 6 (continued)

8 Which of the following rules can be used for this function table?

p	q
5	10
8	16
11	22

F $q = 5 \times p$

G $q = p \times 2$

H $p \div q = 2$

J $p + 5 = q$

9 Which number is represented by *n*?

$$3n + 6 = 30$$

A 4

B 8

C 10

D 12

10 Which number goes in the box to make this number sentence true?

$$(4 + 5) \times 8 = 9 \times \square$$

F 4

G 5

H 8

J 9

11 Krista is 3 times older than Jessica. Krista is 12 years old. How old is Jessica?

A 4

B 9

C 15

D 36

12 Javier and Bill played basketball. Javier scored 4 more than twice the number of points Bill scored. Javier scored 16 points. How many points did Bill score?

F 38

G 10

H 6

J 4

13 What is the value of the expression below?

$$(5 \times 6) \div (4 - 1)$$

A 6

B 10

C 27

D 90

14 $(8 - 3) \times 9 = 9 \times \square$

F 3

G 5

H 8

J 9

Name _____   Date _____

Practice by Chapter
Chapter 7 Multiply by One-Digit Numbers

1 $4,000 \times 5 =$

A 800
B 2,000
C 9,000
D 20,000

2 Miss Lopez bought 4 packs of paper. There are 600 sheets of paper in each pack. How many sheets of paper did she buy?

F 1,200 sheets
G 1,800 sheets
H 2,400 sheets
J 2,800 sheets

3
$$672$$
$$\times\ 9$$

Which is the *best* estimate for the product?

A 700
B 5,400
C 6,300
D 63,000

4 The population of City A is 5,328. There are 6 times as many people living in City B. About how many people live in City B?

F 3,000
G 3,600
H 30,000
J 36,000

5 $87 \times 3 =$

A 241
B 261
C 321
D 341

6
$$52$$
$$\times\ 8$$

F 406
G 408
H 416
J 418

7 Mr. Wilson bought 3 tickets for the amusement park. Each ticket cost $39. How much did Mr. Wilson spend on the tickets?

A $87
B $97
C $117
D $119

8 $483 \times 5 =$

F 2,005
G 2,015
H 2,405
J 2,415

Practice by Chapter
Chapter 7 (continued)

9   924
   × 7

   A 6,348
   B 6,368
   C 6,448
   D 6,468

10   The school auditorium seats 592 people. The band held three concerts in the auditorium. How many people came to see the band play if all the seats were filled for every concert?

   F 1,576
   G 1,596
   H 1,776
   J 1,796

11   308
   × 6

   A 1,808
   B 1,848
   C 1,908
   D 2,208

12   A baseball league sold pizzas to raise money for new uniforms. There are 207 baseball players. Each player sold 8 pizzas. How many pizzas did the league sell in all?

   F 1,606   **H** 1,656
   G 1,615   **J** 2,106

13   6,000 × 7 =

   A 420
   B 4,200
   C 42,000
   D 420,000

14   The debate team sold tickets for a raffle. There are 9 members on the debate team and they each sold 55 tickets. How many tickets did they sell altogether?

   F 440
   G 455
   H 459
   J 495

15   502
   × 5

   A 2,000
   B 2,500
   C 2,510
   D 2,520

16   215 × 9 =

   F 1,895
   G 1,930
   H 1,935
   J 2,135

Practice by Chapter
Chapter 8 Multiply by Two-Digit Numbers

1 $500 \times 80 =$

A 4,000
B 40,000
C 400,000
D 4,000,000

2 There are 32 students in Mr. Ervin's science class. Mr. Ervin took the class to the aquarium. Each ticket cost $10. What was the total cost for the tickets?

F $42
G $320
H $420
J $3,200

3
$$\begin{array}{r} 482 \\ \times\ 71 \end{array}$$

Which is the *best* estimate for the product?

A 2,800
B 3,500
C 28,000
D 35,000

4 The library has 38 boxes of donated books. If there are 25 books in each box, how many books were donated?

F 266
G 810
H 850
J 950

5 $54 \times 23 =$

A 270
B 1,132
C 1,232
D 1,242

6 The Santos family drove from Montana to southern California. They drove at an average speed of 48 miles per hour for 16 hours. About how many miles did the Santos family drive?

F 500 miles
G 800 miles
H 1,000 miles
J 10,000 miles

7 $169 \times 27 =$

A 1,521
B 3,003
C 4,464
D 4,563

8
$$\begin{array}{r} 609 \\ \times\ 54 \end{array}$$

F 32,456
G 32,886
H 32,994
J 33,426

Name _____ Date _____

9 Helene plays the violin. She practices 45 minutes every day. How many minutes does Helene practice the violin in a year? (Hint: 1 year = 365 days)

A 3,285 minutes
B 13,905 minutes
C 16,425 minutes
D 17,225 minutes

10 2,371
  × 82

F 168,222
G 189,422
H 194,422
J 195,222

11 $403.70
  × 26

A $1,049.62
B $3,229.60
C $10,472.20
D $10,496.20

12 Last week, the recycling center collected 1,286 bags of newspaper. If each bag weighs 17 pounds, how many pounds of newspaper did the recycling center collect?

F 19,862
G 20,322
H 21,842
J 21,862

13 23,425
  × 17

A 45,400
B 376,095
C 398,220
D 398,225

14 The school orchestra held 13 concerts last year. If 350 people attended each concert, how many people were at the 13 concerts combined?

F 1,050
G 4,450
H 4,550
J 4,663

15 Carla read 10 books in her English class. Each book had 150 pages. How many pages did Carla read in all?

A 1,500
B 1,510
C 15,000
D 15,100

Practice by Chapter
Chapter 9 Divide by One-Digit Numbers

1 $53 \div 6 =$

A 9

B 8

C 8 R5

D 8 R6

2 Cindy has 4 balls of yarn to knit a scarf. Each ball of yarn is the same size. She has a total of 1,200 feet of yarn. How many feet of yarn is each ball?

F 30 feet

G 300 feet

H 3,000 feet

J 4,800 feet

3 Kyle solved the problem below. Which expression can be used to check his answer?

$$\overset{52r5}{8\overline{)421}}$$

A $(52 \times 8) + 5$

B $(52 \times 5) + 8$

C $(52 + 5) \times 8$

D $(52 + 8) \times 5$

4 $78 \div 3 =$

F 20 R1

G 22 R2

H 22

J 26

5 Which is the *best* estimate for this division expression?

$$7\overline{)361}$$

A 5

B 50

C 60

D 350

6 Rubio has a photo album that holds 96 photos. There are 6 photos on each page. How many pages are in Rubio's photo album?

F 11

G 15

H 16

J 17

7 $4\overline{)583}$

A 120 R3

B 145 R3

C 146

D 158 R1

8 $724 \div 6 =$

F 12

G 12 R4

H 120 R4

J 124

Practice by Chapter
Chapter 9 (continued)

9 Valerie made 8 bracelets. Each bracelet has the same number of beads. If Valerie used a total of 216 beads, how many beads are on each bracelet?

A 20 R2
B 24
C 27
D 28

10 $4,180 \div 5 =$

F 736
G 750
H 836
J 850

11 $3\overline{)80,129}$

A 20,043
B 26,709 R2
C 26,792
D 27,376 R1

12 An annual farm show was held last week. A total of 17,437 people attended the 7-day event. If the same number of people attended each day, what was the daily attendance?

F 2,001
G 2,462
H 2,489
J 2,491

13 $4,569 \div 3 =$

A 923
B 1423
C 1523
D 1533

14 Max solved the problem below. Which expression can be used to check his answer?

$$\begin{array}{r} 773r1 \\ 7\overline{)5412} \end{array}$$

F $(773 \times 1) + 7$
G $(773 \times 7) + 1$
H $(773 + 1) \times 7$
J $(773 + 7) \times 1$

15 Mrs. Baker divided 236 sheets of paper into 4 piles. How many sheets of paper were in each pile?

A 49
B 50
C 58
D 59

16 $4\overline{)57,564}$

F 13,391
G 14,250
H 14,391
J 14,491

Name _____ Date _____

Practice by Chapter
Chapter 10 Geometry

1 Which solid is formed when you fold this net on the dotted lines without overlapping?

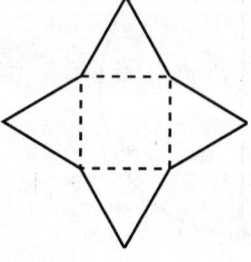

A rectangular prism
B cube
C triangular prism
D pyramid

2 Which of these is a pentagon?

F
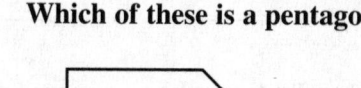

G
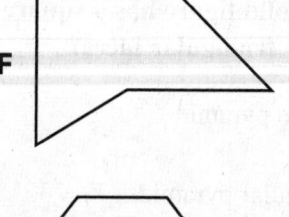

H
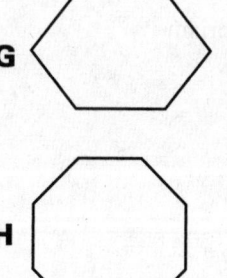

J
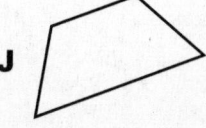

3 Which figures below show a pair of perpendicular lines?

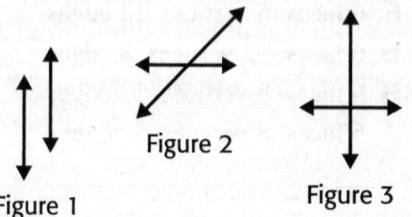

A Figure 1 only
B Figure 3 only
C Figure 2 and Figure 3
D Figure 1 and Figure 2

4 Angle *P* is an obtuse angle. Which could be the measure of ∠*P*?

F 30°
G 80°
H 90°
J 100°

5 What kind of triangle always has 3 sides of different lengths?

A right
B isosceles
C equilateral
D scalene

Name _____ Date _____

Practice by Chapter
Chapter 10 (continued)

6 Which best describes a rectangular prism?

  F 6 faces, 6 vertices, 12 edges
  G 6 faces, 12 vertices, 8 edges
  H 6 faces, 8 vertices, 12 edges
  J 6 faces, 8 vertices, 8 edges

7 Which of the figures below are parallelograms?

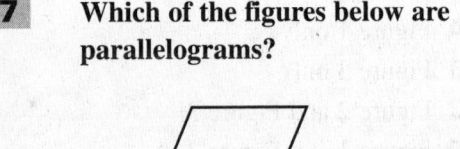
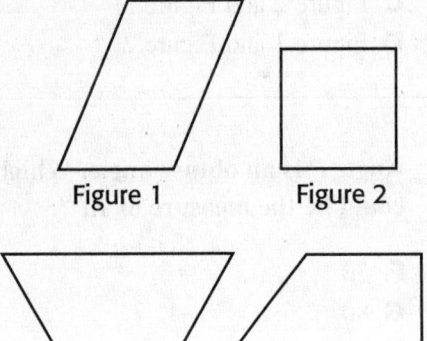
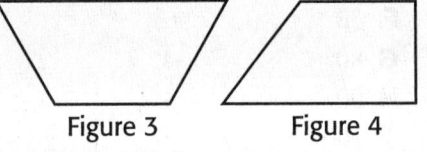

  A Figure 1 only
  B Figure 3 only
  C Figure 1 and Figure 2
  D All the figures are parallelograms.

8 Julia traced one face from three different solid figures to make this pattern. If Julia continues the pattern, which solid figure should she trace next?

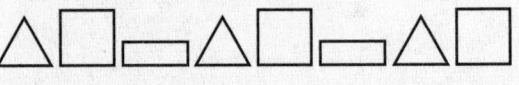

  F triangular pyramid
  G rectangular prism
  H cube
  J sphere

9 Look at the circle with center *J*.

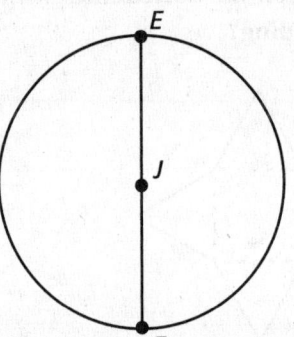

The line segment *EJ* appears to be a

  A radius
  B diameter
  C chord
  D ray

10 Which solid figure has a square base and four triangular faces?

  F square pyramid
  G cube
  H triangular pyramid
  J triangular prism

Name _____ Date _____

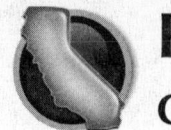

Practice by Chapter
Chapter 11 Geometry and Measurement

1 Look at the figures below. Which figures appear to be congruent?

Figure 1

Figure 2

Figure 3

Figure 4

- **A** Figure 1 and Figure 2
- **B** Figure 1 and Figure 3
- **C** Figures 1, 2, and 3
- **D** None of the figures are congruent.

2 What type of symmetry does this figure have?

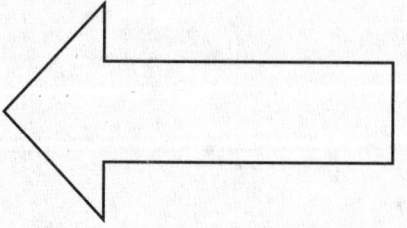

- **F** only bilateral symmetry
- **G** only rotational symmetry
- **H** bilateral and rotational symmetry
- **J** The figure does not have symmetry.

3 A rectangle has a perimeter of 42 meters and a width of 6 meters. What is the length?

- **A** 7 meters
- **B** 15 meters
- **C** 18 meters
- **D** 30 meters

4 Ms. Jones is tiling her laundry room floor. Her laundry room is a square with each side measuring 11 feet. How many 1 foot square tiles does Ms. Jones need to cover the floor?

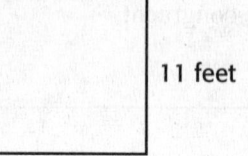

11 feet

- **F** 22
- **G** 44
- **H** 111
- **J** 121

5 Which equation below represents the perimeter (P) of this rectangle in centimeters?

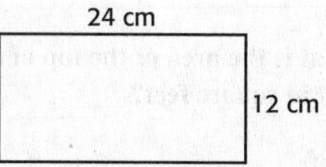

24 cm

12 cm

- **A** $P = 24 \times 12$
- **B** $P = 24 + 12$
- **C** $P = (2 + 24) \times (2 + 12)$
- **D** $P = (2 \times 24) + (2 \times 12)$

Practice by Chapter
Chapter 11 (continued)

---

6 Which statement about the figures is true?

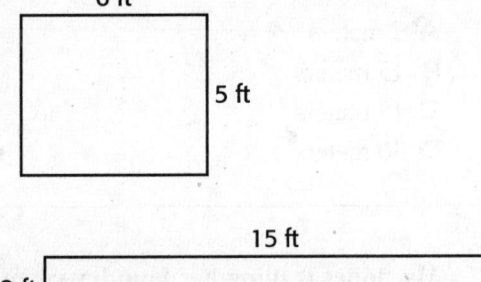

6 ft

5 ft

15 ft

2 ft

F They have the same area.
G They have the same perimeter.
H They have the same length.
J They are congruent.

---

7 Bobby's father is building a brick wall around their fireplace. Here is a diagram of the top of the brick wall.

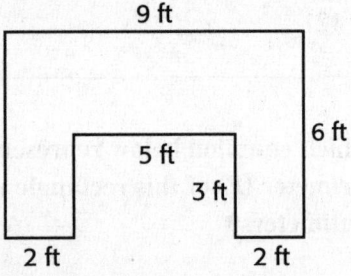

9 ft

5 ft

6 ft

3 ft

2 ft   2 ft

What is the area of the top of the brick wall in square feet?

A 30
B 39
C 41
D 57

---

8 Look at the rectangles below. Which rectangle has a perimeter of 28 inches and an area of 24 inches?

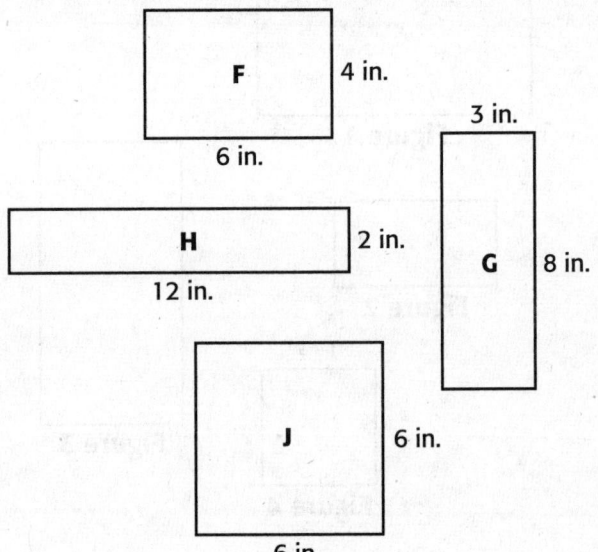

F   4 in.

6 in.

3 in.

H   2 in.

12 in.

G   8 in.

J   6 in.

6 in.

F F
G G
H H
J J

Name _____ Date _____

Practice by Chapter
Chapter 12 Algebra and Graphing

1 Which symbol is located at ⁻1 on the number line below?

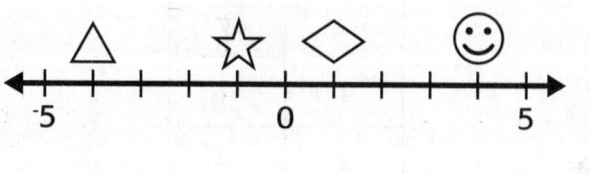

A △

B ☆

C ◇

D ☺

2 Look at the map below. Which location has the coordinates (2, 5)?

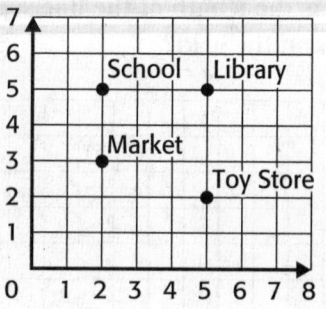

F Toy Store
G Market
H Library
J School

3 Look at the line segment shown below.

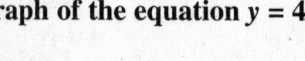

What is the length of the line segment?

A 2 units
B 4 units
C 5 units
D 6 units

4 Look at the problem below.

$$x = 3y + 1$$

If $y = 4$, what is x?

F 1
G 11
H 12
J 13

5 Which of the following points is on the graph of the equation $y = 4x$?

A (4, 1)
B (2, 8)
C (3, 7)
D (1, 3)

Practice by Chapter
Chapter 12 (continued)

6   Arnold plotted 4 points on a grid. The 4 points were all on the same straight line.

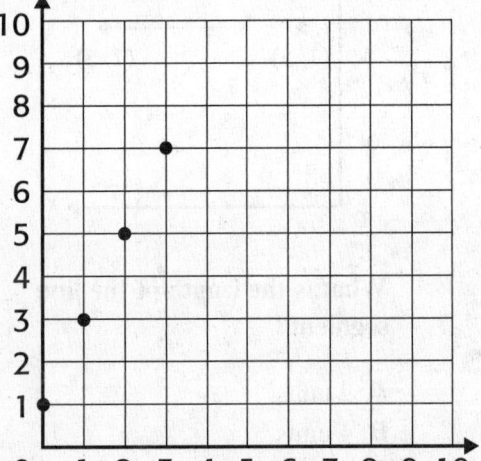

If he plots another point on the line, what could be its coordinates?

F (4, 9)
G (5, 10)
H (9, 4)
J (5, 9)

7   Look at the problem below.

$$x = 2y - 3$$

If $y = 6$, what is x?

A 3
B 6
C 9
D 12

8   Look at the *x* and *y* values in the function table.

x	y
1	1
2	4
3	7
4	10

Which equation below is the rule for the table?

F $y = x$
G $y = 2x$
H $y = 3x - 2$
J $y = 2x + 1$

9   What is the length of the line segment shown on the grid?

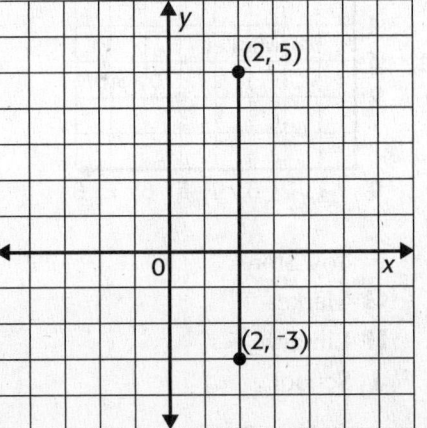

A 5
B 7
C 8
D 12

Practice by Chapter
Chapter 13 Fractions

1 Which fraction represents the shaded part of the figure?

A $\frac{1}{6}$

B $\frac{1}{5}$

C $\frac{5}{6}$

D $\frac{5}{1}$

2 Which fraction represents the smallest part of a whole?

F $\frac{1}{2}$

G $\frac{1}{3}$

H $\frac{1}{8}$

J $\frac{1}{10}$

3 Which of the following is *true*?

A $\frac{7}{8} = 1\frac{1}{7}$

B $\frac{3}{4} = \frac{6}{12}$

C $\frac{3}{5} > \frac{6}{15}$

D $\frac{1}{2} < \frac{5}{10}$

4 A pet store has animals for adoption. There are 6 cats and 2 dogs at the store.

What fraction of the animals are cats?

F $\frac{3}{4}$

G $\frac{1}{3}$

H $\frac{1}{4}$

J $\frac{1}{6}$

5 Which is equivalent to $\frac{8}{10}$?

A $\frac{1}{3}$

B $\frac{3}{5}$

C $\frac{4}{5}$

D $\frac{10}{12}$

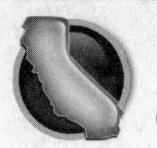

Practice by Chapter
Chapter 13 (continued)

---

6 What fraction is best represented by point *C* on this number line?

C
0 ———————— 1.0

F $\frac{3}{10}$

G $\frac{1}{3}$

H $\frac{3}{7}$

J $\frac{7}{10}$

---

7 $\frac{4}{5} + \frac{3}{5} =$

A $\frac{1}{5}$

B $\frac{7}{10}$

C $\frac{5}{7}$

D $1\frac{2}{5}$

---

8 Emma and her friends shared a pizza. There is $\frac{1}{6}$ of the pizza left. Which picture shows this?

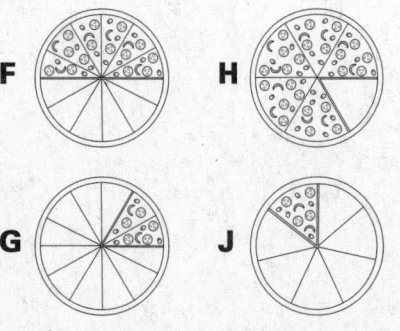

---

9 On the number line below, what number does point *Z* represent?

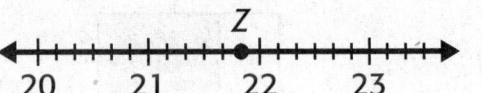

A $21\frac{1}{5}$

B $21\frac{5}{6}$

C $22\frac{1}{6}$

D $22\frac{5}{6}$

---

10 Which fraction represents the shaded part of the figure?

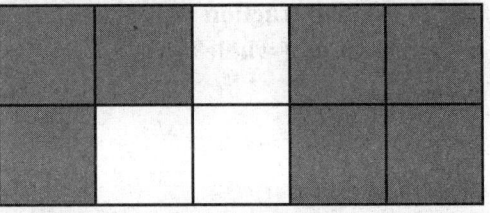

F $\frac{3}{10}$

G $\frac{1}{2}$

H $\frac{7}{10}$

J $\frac{4}{5}$

Practice by Chapter
Chapter 14 Decimals

1 Which fraction means the same as 0.3?

A $\frac{3}{1}$

B $\frac{3}{10}$

C $\frac{3}{100}$

D $\frac{3}{1000}$

2 Scott used $\frac{3}{4}$ cup of milk in his cereal this morning. What is another way to write this amount?

F 0.25

G 0.34

H 0.68

J 0.75

3 Which decimal means the same as $5\frac{1}{2}$?

A 5.5

B 5.25

C 5.2

D 5.12

4 Which of the following has the greatest value?

F 0.42

G 1.5

H 10.1

J 3.04

5 In gym class the students ran a lap around the track. The coach recorded the students' times in a table.

Name	Time (minutes)
Johnny	3.08
Pilar	2.82
Tyler	2.4
Jonas	3.30

Which student ran the fastest?

A Johnny

B Pilar

C Tyler

D Jonas

6 What number is represented by point A on this number line?

F 3.04

G 3.4

H 3.6

J 4.6

Practice by Chapter
Chapter 14 (continued)

7 Gina made a scarf that was 1.2 meters long.

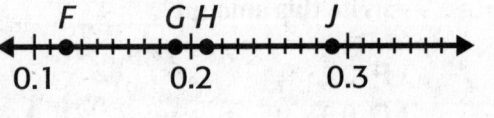

Which of the following is equivalent to this number?

A $1\frac{1}{2}$

B $1\frac{4}{10}$

C $1\frac{2}{10}$

D $1\frac{2}{100}$

8 Which of the following is *true*?

F $\frac{1}{4} = 2.5$

G $\frac{1}{6} = 1.6$

H $\frac{9}{5} < 1.4$

J $\frac{18}{10} > 0.18$

9 Which of the following are in order from least to greatest?

A $1\frac{7}{10}$, 1.08, $\frac{4}{10}$, 0.29

B $\frac{4}{10}$, 0.29, $1\frac{7}{10}$, 1.08

C 0.29, $\frac{4}{10}$, 1.08, $1\frac{7}{10}$

D $\frac{4}{10}$, $1\frac{7}{10}$, 1.08, 0.29

10 Which point is located at 0.21 on the number line?

```
        F        G H            J
  ←—•——————————•—•——————————•———————→
   0.1        0.2           0.3
```

F F

G G

H H

J J

11 Which fraction means the same as 0.75?

A $\frac{1}{4}$

B $\frac{1}{2}$

C $\frac{3}{5}$

D $\frac{3}{4}$

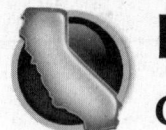

Name _____   Date _____

Practice by Chapter
Chapter 15 Decimals: Addition and Subtraction

1 The height of the Washington Monument is 169.29 meters. What is the height of the monument rounded to the nearest whole number?

A 160
B 169
C 170
D 200

2 What is 56.84 rounded to the nearest tenth?

F 56.8
G 56.9
H 57
J 60

3 The US Bank Tower in Los Angeles is 310.3 meters high. The Golden Gate Bridge is 227.40 meters high. About how much taller is the US Bank Tower than the Golden Gate Bridge?

A 80 meters
B 110 meters
C 117 meters
D 500 meters

4 $34.72 + 8.69 =$

F 26.03
G 32.31
H 43.41
J 121.62

5 Look at the map below.

2.25 miles — Lynn's House — 1.8 miles — Library
2 miles
2.1 miles — School
4.7 miles
Playground

Lynn biked from her house to the library and then took the bike trail to the playground. Approximately how many miles did Lynn bike?

A 7 miles
B 8 miles
C 9 miles
D 13 miles

6 Mrs. Asher is sewing a dress for her daughter. She used 1.75 meters of red fabric and 2.3 meters of white fabric. How much fabric did Mrs. Asher use in all to make the dress?

F 4.05 m
G 3.05 m
H 1.98 m
J 1.45 m

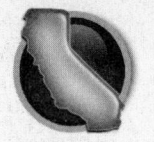

Practice by Chapter
Chapter 15 (continued)

7 25.04
  − 11.72

    A 13.32
    B 14.32
    C 14.72
    D 36.76

8 Tom and Brad are both on the swim team. They competed in the 50-meter freestyle. Tom's time was 35.72 seconds. Brad's time was 29.6 seconds. How much faster was Brad's time?

    F 6.12 seconds
    G 16.12 seconds
    H 32.76 seconds
    J 65.32 seconds

9 Irene bought a book, a puzzle, and a box of markers at the store. She spent a total of $32.08. The puzzle cost $9.58 and the markers cost $5. What was the cost of the book?

    A $17.50
    B $22.45
    C $27.50
    D $32.50

10 12.36 + 14.25 =

    F 26.51
    G 26.52
    H 26.61
    J 27.61

11 Elias and a group of friends went to a park to go hiking. The chart shows the length of the different hiking trails at the park.

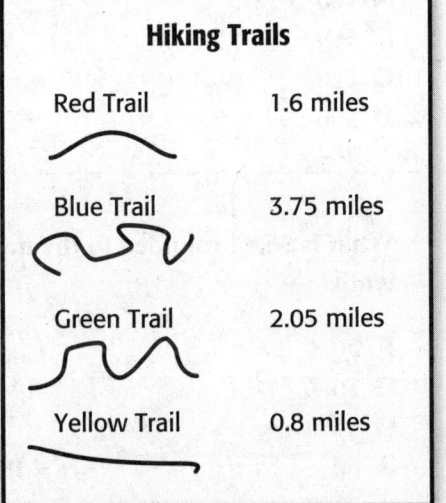

Hiking Trails	
Red Trail	1.6 miles
Blue Trail	3.75 miles
Green Trail	2.05 miles
Yellow Trail	0.8 miles

If Elias and his friends hike all four trails, how many total miles will they have hiked?

    A 6.04 miles
    B 6.1 miles
    C 7.49 miles
    D 8.2 miles

12 17.33
  −12.98

    F 4.35
    G 4.45
    H 5.35
    J 5.45

Practice by Chapter
Chapter 16 Probability

1 There are 10 red gumballs, 8 blue gumballs, 12 white gumballs, and 2 yellow gumballs in a box. Jeff reaches into the box without looking and picks a gumball. Which color gumball is he most likely to choose?

A red
B blue
C white
D yellow

2 Look at this spinner.

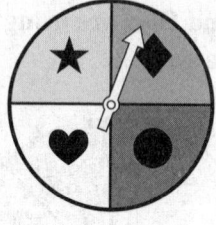

How many outcomes are possible if you spin the spinner and toss a number cube with sides 1, 2, 3, 4, 5, and 6?

F 6
G 10
H 12
J 24

3 A teacher has a bag of 12 lollipops. The table shows the number of each flavor.

Flavor	Number of lollipops
Orange	3
Lemon	2
Cherry	5
Watermelon	2

Oscar's favorite flavor is cherry. If he reaches into the bag without looking, what is the probability that he will pick a cherry lollipop?

A 1 out of 4
B 1 out of 5
C 1 out of 12
D 5 out of 12

4 Ten tiles numbered 1 through 10 are put in a bag. A student reaches into the bag without looking and picks a tile from the bag. Which of the following is true?

F It is most likely the tile is an even number.
G It is most likely the tile is an odd number.
H It is equally likely that the tile is an even number or an odd number.
J 1 out of 10 tiles is an even number.

Practice by Chapter
Chapter 16 (continued)

5 At a deli, you can make your own sandwich. The menu shows your choices for bread, meat, and cheese.

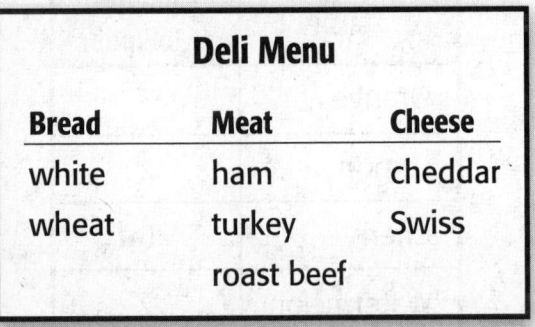

Deli Menu

Bread	Meat	Cheese
white	ham	cheddar
wheat	turkey	Swiss
	roast beef	

If you select only one item from each category, how many possible combinations are there?

A 6
B 7
C 10
D 12

6 Mark is doing a probability experiment. He tosses a two-sided coin and a number cube. The cube is numbered 1 through 6. He uses a table to record the outcome of each toss. How many possible outcomes are listed in his table?

F 6
G 8
H 10
J 12

7 Cho has a bin filled with colored blocks. There are 4 red blocks and 8 blue blocks. All the blocks are the same size. If she pulls out 1 block without looking, what is the probability that it will be a red block?

A $\frac{1}{2}$

B $\frac{1}{3}$

C $\frac{1}{4}$

D $\frac{1}{12}$

8 Ayala and Diaz are using this spinner to play a game.

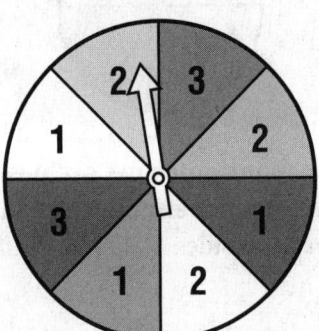

To win the game, Ayala needs to spin a 2. What is the probability of spinning a 2?

F $\frac{1}{8}$

G $\frac{1}{3}$

H $\frac{3}{8}$

J $\frac{3}{4}$

Name: _____ Date: _____

Periodic Assessment 1
Chapters 1–4

1 Which of these is the number 4,306,287?

A four million, three hundred six thousand, two hundred eighty-seven

B four million, three hundred sixty thousand, two hundred eighty-seven

C forty-three million, six thousand, two hundred eighty-seven

D four billion, three hundred six thousand, two hundred eighty-seven

2 Which digit is in the thousands place in the number 2,743,921?

F 2

G 3

H 4

J 9

3 What is the number six million, four hundred thousand, eight hundred twenty-two in standard form?

A 640,822

B 6,004,822

C 6,400,822

D 6,408,022

4 Which of the following has the least value?

F 267,463

G 301,296

H 212,241

J 289,000

5 Look at the problem below.

$$x = y + 9$$

If $y = 5$, what is x?

A 4

B 14

C 15

D 45

6 Katie borrowed $10 from Megan last week. This week, Katie paid Megan $8. How much money does Katie owe Megan now?

F $2

G $8

H $10

J $18

7 What is 198,462 rounded to the nearest ten?

A 198,000

B 198,460

C 198,500

D 200,000

8 The population of a city is 344,201. What is this number rounded to the nearest thousand?

F 344,000

G 344,200

H 340,000

J 300,000

Name _____ Date _____

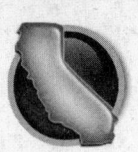 # Periodic Assessment 1 (continued)

9 What is 54,872,918 rounded to the nearest hundred thousand?

A 54,870,000
B 54,872,900
C 54,900,000
D 55,000,000

10 The sum of x plus y equals 30. If $x = 9$, which equation can be used to find the value of y?

F $9 + x = 30$
G $y + 9 = 30$
H $x - y = 30$
J $y - 9 = 30$

11 Mrs. Brandt is ordering buses for the field trip. Each bus holds 40 students and there are 50 students going on the trip. How many buses does Mrs. Brandt need?

A 1 **C** 3
B 2 **D** 4

12 What is 32,876,512 rounded to the nearest hundred thousand?

F 30,000,000
G 32,876,500
H 32,900,000
J 33,000,000

13 The sum of a plus b equals 32. If $a = 12$, what is the value of b?

A 20
B 22
C 44
D 384

14 Estimate the difference of $6407 - 2658$ by rounding to the nearest hundred.

F 3000
G 3400
H 3700
J 9400

15 Estimate the sum of $7521 + 3432$ by rounding to the nearest thousand.

A 4000
B 10,000
C 11,000
D 12,000

16 $3276 + 1718 =$

F 1558
G 4894
H 4984
J 4994

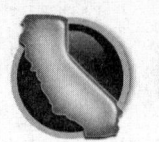

Periodic Assessment 1 (continued)

17   4197
        + 3061

   A 1136
   B 7158
   C 7258
   D 8258

18 9324 − 562 =

   F 8762
   G 8862
   H 9762
   J 9886

19 Which of the following equations is *not* true?

   A 8 + (5 − 4) = 8 + 1
   B 3 + (6 × 2) = 3 + 12
   C 7 + (8 − 4) = 15 + 4
   D 10 + (3 × 2) = 10 + 6

20 Which of the following equations is true?

   F 3 + (12 − 5) = 3 + (5 − 12)
   G 18 − (2 + 1) = (18 − 2) + 1
   H 25 + (6 ÷ 2) = (25 + 6) ÷ 2
   J 24 + (8 + 3) = 24 + 8 + 3

21 34 + 10 = 34 + ☐

   A (9 × 1)   **C** (4 × 6)
   B (2 × 5)   **D** (3 × 7)

22 9816 − 3243 =

   F 6573
   G 6673
   H 7573
   J 13059

23 Dwight was comparing the population of some large cities. The bar graph below shows what he learned.

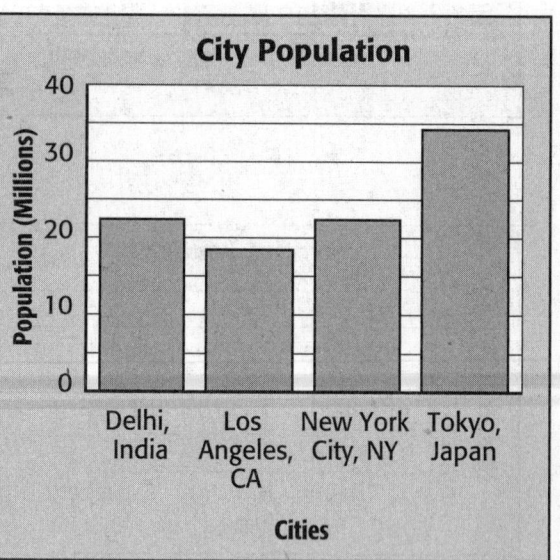

Which two cities' population seems to be the same?

   A Delhi and Los Angeles
   B Delhi and New York City
   C New York City and Tokyo
   D Los Angeles and New York City

Periodic Assessment 1 (continued)

24 Edward surveyed his class about their favorite food. Of the 50 students, 12 voted for pizza, 15 voted for hot dogs, and 23 voted for spaghetti.

Which of the following bar graphs represents the survey?

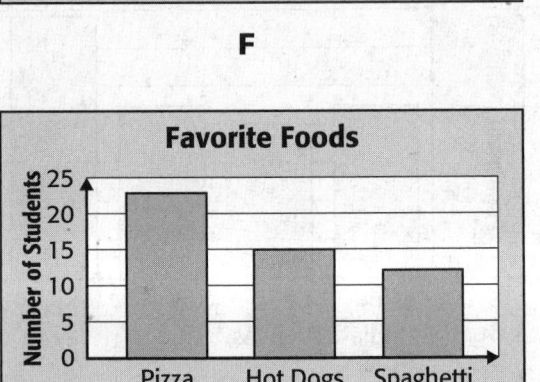

F

G

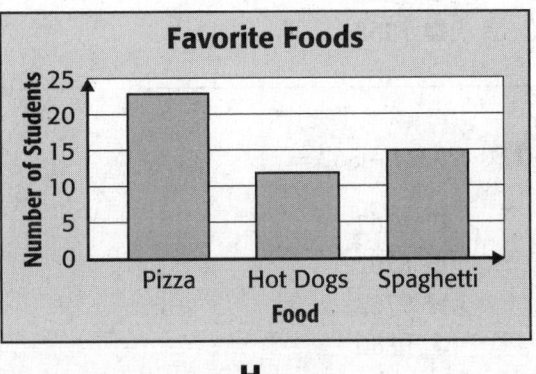

H

J

Periodic Assessment 1 (continued)

25 Identify the median of the data.

3, 10, 9, 7, 5, 21, 16, 15, 8

A 5
B 8
C 9
D 10

26 The graph below represents the weather for the previous two school years. Which of the following is true about the graph?

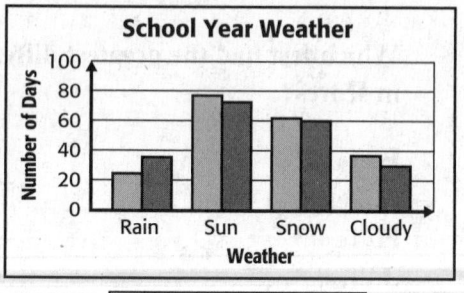

School Year Weather

2004-2005   2005-2006

F It rained more in 2004–2005 than in 2005–2006.
G It was sunny more days in 2004–2005 than it was in 2005–2006.
H There were more snowy days in 2005–2006 than in 2004–2005.
J There were more rainy days in 2004–2005 than there were cloudy days in 2004–2005.

27 The line graph below represents the high temperatures for the week. Which day had the lowest temperature?

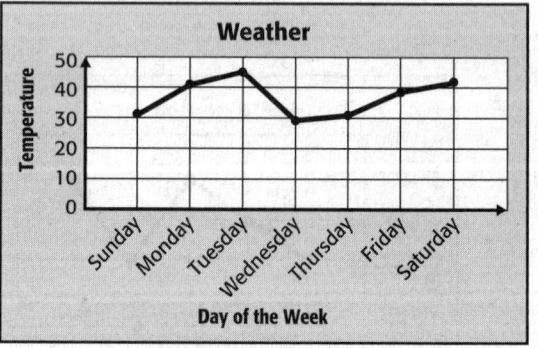

A Sunday
B Tuesday
C Wednesday
D Saturday

28 Identify the mode of the data.

13, 17, 18, 14, 21, 14, 15

F 14
G 15
H 16
J 21

Periodic Assessment 1 (continued)

29 The graph below represents candy sales for each grade at an elementary school. How much more did the fourth grade make than the third grade?

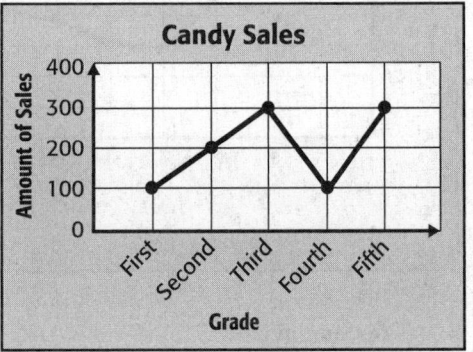

Candy Sales

Amount of Sales: 0, 100, 200, 300, 400
Grade: First, Second, Third, Fourth, Fifth

A $50
B $100
C $125
D $200

30 The following bar graph represents average scores for math tests in two sixth grade classes.

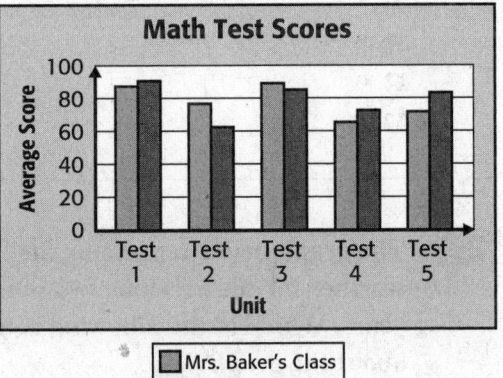

Math Test Scores

Average Score: 0, 20, 40, 60, 80, 100
Unit: Test 1, Test 2, Test 3, Test 4, Test 5

■ Mrs. Baker's Class
■ Mr. Fisher's Class

Which test had the greatest difference in scores?

F Test 1
G Test 2
H Test 3
J Test 5

31 Marcus went to the movies. His ticket cost $6.50, his popcorn cost $2.75, and his drink cost $1.25. Marcus estimates that he spent about $9.00. Is his estimate a good estimate? Explain.

Stop

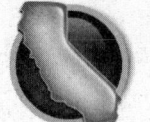

Periodic Assessment 2
Chapters 1–8

1 What is 54,918 rounded to the nearest thousand?

   A 50,000
   B 54,900
   C 54,920
   D 55,000

2 Cindy bought 10 bags of peanuts to make trail mix. If each bag has 15 peanuts, what is the greatest number of peanuts Cindy's recipe will contain?

   F 5 peanuts
   G 25 peanuts
   H 50 peanuts
   J 150 peanuts

3 A bakery needs 24 cups of nuts to make cookies. If one bag of nuts holds 3 cups of nuts, how many bags of nuts will the bakery need?

   A 6
   B 7
   C 8
   D 21

4 $47 \times 208 =$

   F 9776
   G 9400
   H 255
   J 161

5 $38 \times 185 =$

   A 555
   B 703
   C 5550
   D 7030

6 Jamie needs 50 slices of pizza for the basketball team. If each pizza has 8 slices, how many pizzas does Jamie need?

   F 6
   G 7
   H 50
   J 58

7 The cost for admission to a concert is $23 for each ticket. If a total of 143 tickets are sold, what is the total amount of money from ticket sales?

   A $23
   B $120
   C $166
   D $3289

8 Bobby is loading bags of gravel on a truck. Each bag weighs 42 pounds. How many pounds do 134 bags weigh?

   F 92
   G 176
   H 562
   J 5628

 **Periodic Assessment 2** (continued)

9 Which of these is another way to write the product 16 × 4?

A 2 × 8 × 2

B 10 × 2

C 2 × 8 × 4

D 4 × 4 × 8

10 There are 238 students at Jordan Elementary School participating in a fundraiser. If each student sells $15 worth of cookies, how much money will the school collect?

F $3570

G $357

H $253

J $223

11 Which statement is true?

A The only factors of 6 are 1 and 6.

B The only factors of 7 are 1 and 7.

C The only factors of 8 are 1 and 8.

D The only factors of 9 are 1 and 9.

12 Which is a prime number?

F 4

G 5

H 6

J 8

13 Micah read 92 pages of a 176 page book. Write an equation to show how many pages Micah needs to read to finish the book. Use the variable p in your equation.

A $176 = p - 92$

B $176 + p = 84$

C $84 - p = 176$

D $p + 92 = 176$

14 Which number is represented by t?

$$104 \div t = 2$$

F 52

G 102

H 106

J 208

15 What is the value of the expression below?

$$(5 × 4) + (6 × 2)$$

A 32

B 52

C 80

D 240

16 If $y = (a + b) - c$, and a is 12, b is 10 and c is 6, what is the value of y?

F 4

G 8

H 16

J 114

Periodic Assessment 2 (continued)

17 What is the value of g?

$$g = (11 \times 3) - (14 \div 2)$$

A 0

B 19

C $\frac{19}{2}$

D 26

18 What is the value of the expression below if $f = 6$?

$$47 - (13 + f)$$

F 28

G 34

H 40

J 60

19 $(18 \div 6) \times (12 - 7) =$

A 15

B 19

C 29

D 89

20 $21 \times (12 - 4) =$

F 29

G 168

H 252

J 1008

21 The sum of x plus y equals 32. If $x = 10$, what is the value of y?

A 22

B 32

C 42

D 320

22 $17 \times (15 + 3) =$

F 1

G 85

H 258

J 306

23 If $b = 3a + 9$ and $a = 4$, what is the value of b?

A 31

B 21

C 16

D 12

24 The sum of a and b equals 41. If $a = 21$, what is the value of b?

F 20

G 21

H 62

J 861

25 $62 + 18 = 62 + \square$

A $3 + 6$ **C** 2×12

B 3×6 **D** 4×4

Periodic Assessment 2 (continued)

26 Which statement is true?

    F $(8 + 4) + 3 = 12 + 3$

    G $(8 + 4) + 3 = 7 + 1 + 4$

    H $(8 + 4) + 3 = 8(4 + 3)$

    J $(8 + 4) + 3 = 8 \times 4 + 3$

27 Which equation is true?

    A $7(3 + 1) = 7 \times 3 + 1$

    B $7(3 + 1) = 7(2 + 2)$

    C $7(3 + 1) = 7 + 3 + 1$

    D $7(3 + 1) = 7 \times 1 + 3$

28 Which equation is true?

    F $3 + (16 - 5) = 3 + (5 - 16)$

    G $15 - (2 + 1) = (15 - 2) + 1$

    H $32 + (8 \div 4) = (32 + 8) \div 4$

    J $24 + (9 - 3) = 24 + 9 - 3$

29 What number goes in the box to make this number sentence true?

$$(8 - 4) \times 3 = 4 \times \square$$

    A 2

    B 3

    C 4

    D 12

30 On Friday Mr. Gomez drove 104 miles, on Saturday he drove 72 miles, and on Sunday he drove 101 miles. Approximately how many miles did Mr. Gomez drive in the three days?

    F 100 miles

    G 200 miles

    H 300 miles

    J 400 miles

31 Solve. Explain how you can use multiplication to check your answer.

$$967 \div 8$$

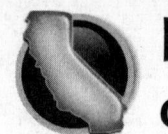

Name   Date

Periodic Assessment 3
Chapters 1–12

1 $7\overline{)3521}$

    A 530
    B 503
    C 350
    D 305

2 Jackie solved the problem below.

$$9\overline{)4628}\;\;514r2$$

Which expression could be used to check her answer?

    F $(4628 \times 9) + 514$
    G $(9 \times 514) - 2$
    H $(9 \times 2) + 514$
    J $(9 \times 514) + 2$

3 Which equation below represents the area (A) of the rectangle in square feet?

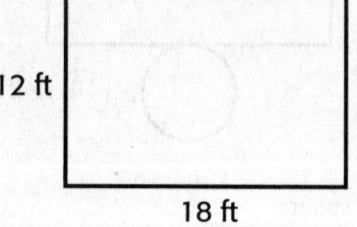

12 ft

18 ft

    A $A = 12 \times 18$
    B $A = 12 + 18$
    C $A = 12 + 12 + 18 + 18$
    D $A = 12 + 12 \times 18 + 18$

4 There are 9 pencils in one box. Sharice bought 414 pencils. How many boxes of pencils did she buy?

    F 46
    G 405
    H 423
    J 3726

5 There are 8 calculators in each box. Mr. Martinez ordered 408 calculators. How many boxes did he order?

    A 3264
    B 416
    C 400
    D 51

6 A toy company sent puzzles to 7 different toy stores. The company sent 588 puzzles in all. How many puzzles were sent to each toy store?

    F 84
    G 581
    H 595
    J 4116

7 Which type of triangle always has 3 sides of equal length?

    A isosceles
    B scalene
    C right
    D equilateral

Periodic Assessment 3 (continued)

8 $8\overline{)2496}$

    F 302

    G 312

    H 412

    J 422

9 Which two figures below appear to be congruent?

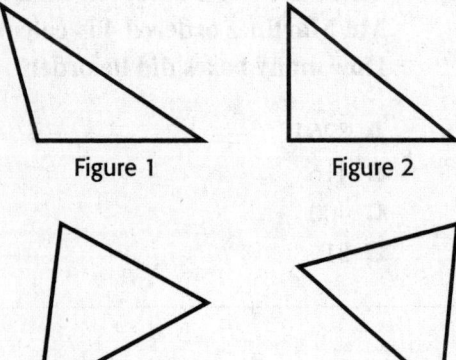

Figure 1   Figure 2

Figure 3   Figure 4

    A Figures 1 and 2

    B Figures 3 and 4

    C Figures 2 and 4

    D Figures 2 and 3

10 Which equation below represents the area (A) of the rectangle in square meters?

7 m | 13 m

    F $A = 13 + 13 + 7 + 7$

    G $A = 13 + 13 \times 7 + 7$

    H $A = 7 \times 13$

    J $A = 7 + 13$

11 Which figure can be formed by this pattern when it is folded without overlapping?

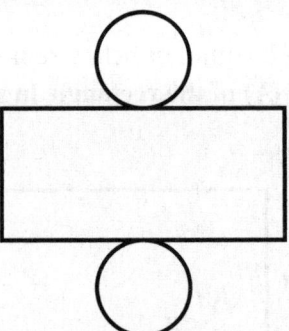

    A sphere

    B cube

    C cylinder

    D pyramid

Periodic Assessment 3 (continued)

12 What is the area of this rectangle?

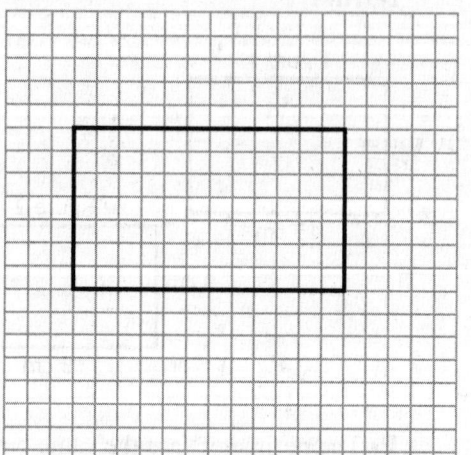

1 block = 1 square mile

- **F** 38 square miles
- **G** 72 square miles
- **H** 84 square miles
- **J** 100 square miles

13 The length of a garden is 8 feet and the width is 6 feet. What is the area of the garden?

- **A** 14 square feet
- **B** 28 square feet
- **C** 36 square feet
- **D** 48 square feet

14 Which quadrilateral always has 2 sides that are parallel and 2 sides that are not parallel?

- **F** square
- **G** trapezoid
- **H** rectangle
- **J** rhombus

15 How many 90° angles are in this figure?

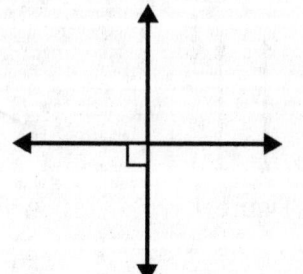

- **A** one
- **B** two
- **C** three
- **D** four

16 Which statement about the figures below is true?

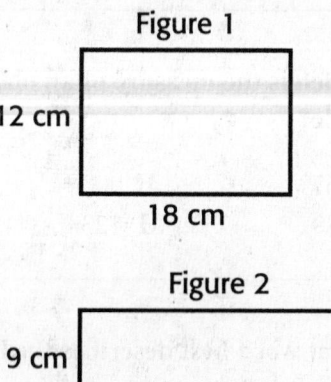

Figure 1

12 cm

18 cm

Figure 2

9 cm

24 cm

- **F** The area of Figure 1 is greater than the area of Figure 2.
- **G** The area of Figure 2 is greater than the area of Figure 1.
- **H** The perimeters of both figures are the same.
- **J** The areas of both figures are the same.

Name　　　　　　　　　　　　　　　　　Date

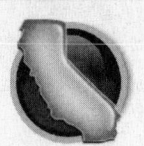 # Periodic Assessment 3 (continued)

17 Which figures below show pairs of lines that appear to be perpendicular?

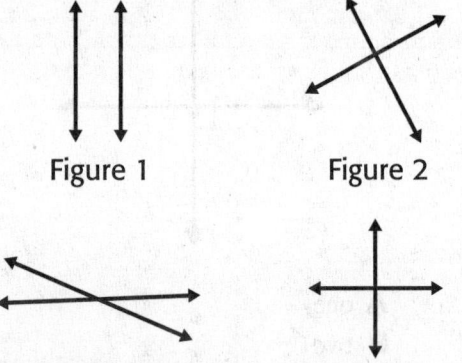

Figure 1　　　　　Figure 2

Figure 3　　　　　Figure 4

A Figure 1 only
B Figure 2 only
C Figures 1 and 4
D Figures 2 and 4

18 Which is the measure of an obtuse angle?

F 67°　　　　H 90°
G 89°　　　　J 123°

19 What word best describes the lines below?

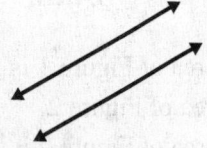

A perpendicular
B parallel
C intersecting
D straight

20 Which statement about the figures is true?

Figure 1
10 cm
15 cm

Figure 2
9 cm
16 cm

F The perimeters are the same but the areas are different.
G The perimeter of Figure 2 is larger.
H The areas are the same but the perimeters are different.
J The perimeter and area of both figures are the same.

21 Two sides of an isosceles triangle are 12 cm and 15 cm. What are the possible lengths of the third side?

A 3 cm or 12 cm
B 12 cm or 15 cm
C 12 cm or 27 cm
D 15 cm or 27 cm

22 Which quadrilateral *always* has 4 right angles and 4 sides the same length?

F rhombus
G rectangle
H trapezoid
J square

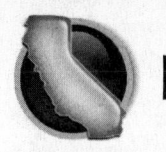

Periodic Assessment 3 (continued)

23 Look at the circle with center *O*.

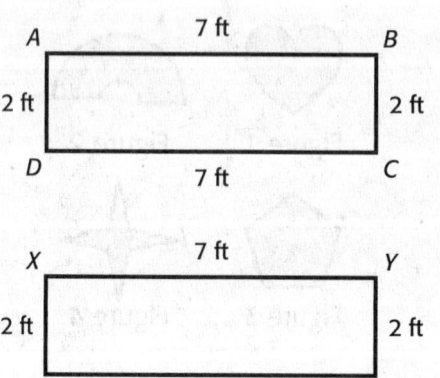

The line segment *ON* appears to be

A a diameter
B an arc
C a radius
D an area

24 What length of side $\overline{AC}$ will make the triangles congruent?

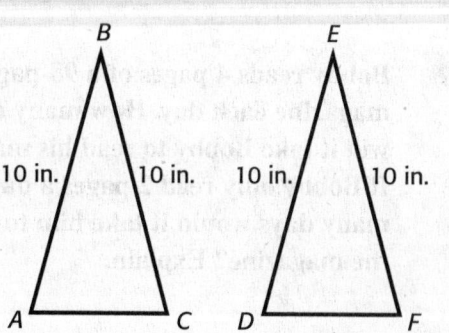

F 6 in.
G 10 in.
H 16 in.
J 20 in.

25 Which statement about the figures is true?

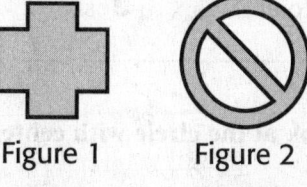

A The figures have different perimeters.
B The figures have different areas.
C The figures are congruent.
D The figures do not have line symmetry.

26 Which figures have bilateral symmetry?

Figure 1   Figure 2

Figure 3   Figure 4

F Figure 1 only
G Figure 3 only
H Figures 1, 2 and 3
J Figures 1 and 3

 # Periodic Assessment 3 (continued)

27 Which figures have rotational symmetry?

Figure 1   Figure 2

Figure 3   Figure 4

A Figures 3 and 4
B Figure 2 only
C Figure 1 only
D Figures 1 and 2

28 How many triangular faces does a square pyramid have?

F three   **H** five
G four   **J** six

29 Look at the circle with center *O*.

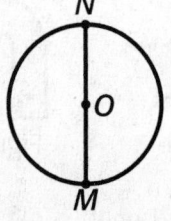

The line segment *MN* is

A an arc   **C** a radius
B a diameter   **D** a perimeter

30 What is the area of this pee-wee football field?

GIANTS

GIANTS

1 block = 1 square yard

F 18 square yards
G 36 square yards
H 80 square yards
J 324 square yards

31 Bobby reads 4 pages of a 98-page magazine each day. How many days will it take Bobby to read his magazine? If Bobby only read 2 pages a day, how many days would it take him to read the magazine? Explain.

Stop

Copyright © Macmillan/McGraw-Hill, a division of The McGraw-Hill Companies, Inc.

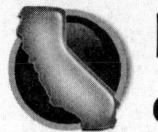

Periodic Assessment 4
Chapters 1–16

1 What fraction of this circle is shaded?

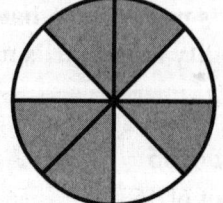

A $\frac{6}{7}$

B $\frac{6}{8}$

C $\frac{5}{7}$

D $\frac{5}{8}$

2 Mark needs 45 cups of popcorn to make popcorn balls. If one bag makes 6 cups, how many bags does Mark need?

F 6

G 7

H 8

J 9

3 Which is a fraction for the figures modeled below?

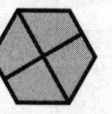 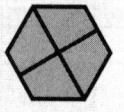 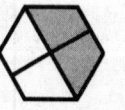

A $\frac{3}{2}$

B $3\frac{1}{2}$

C $\frac{5}{2}$

D $3\frac{2}{4}$

4 Which of the following fractions is *not* equivalent to $\frac{3}{4}$?

F $\frac{9}{12}$

G $\frac{2}{4}$

H $\frac{6}{8}$

J $\frac{75}{100}$

5 Look at the line segment shown below.

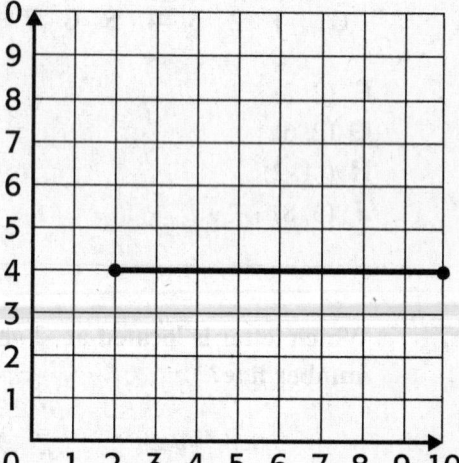

What is the length of the line segment?

A 4 units

B 8 units

C 9 units

D 10 units

Periodic Assessment 4 (continued)

6 Which point is on this line?

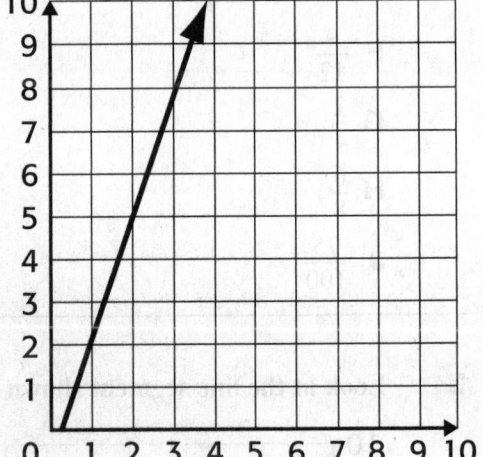

F (2, 2)
G (2, 6)
H (⁻1, 2)
J (3, 8)

7 Which letter is located at ⁻2 on the number line?

A *W*
B *X*
C *Y*
D *Z*

8 There are 15 boys and 14 girls in Mrs. Hawkins' class. If she puts each student's name into a hat, what is the probability that a girl's name will be pulled?

F 1 out of 15
G 14 out of 15
H 14 out of 29
J 15 out of 29

9 Which of the following shows $\frac{2}{3}$ of the rectangle shaded?

A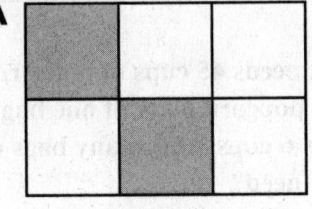

B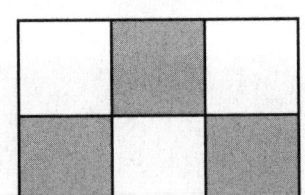

C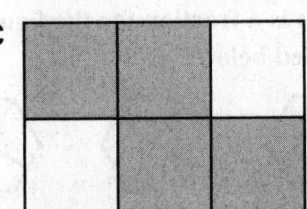

D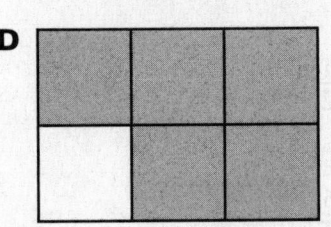

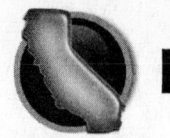

Periodic Assessment 4 (continued)

10 Which of the following numbers has the greatest value?

F 8.71 **H** 5.04

G 7.92 **J** 3.49

11 Which fraction means the same as 0.27?

A $\frac{100}{27}$ **C** $\frac{1}{27}$

B $\frac{27}{10}$ **D** $\frac{27}{100}$

12 Which fraction is equivalent to 0.5?

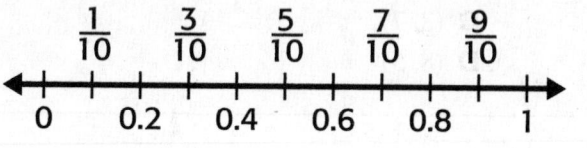

F $\frac{9}{10}$

G $\frac{7}{10}$

H $\frac{5}{10}$

J $\frac{3}{10}$

13 Point A is at (7, 2) and Point B is at (10, 2). How can you find the length of AB?

A Add 7 and 10

B Add 2 and 2

C Subtract 10 and 7

D Subtract 2 and 2

14 Which of the following statements is true?

F 3.56 < 3.34

G 9.44 > 10.02

H 12.22 < 15.57

J 8.56 > 8.65

15 Order the set of numbers from least to greatest.

3.42, 6.12, 2.89, 4.96

A 6.12, 4.96, 3.42, 2.89

B 3.42, 6.12, 2.89, 4.96

C 2.89, 3.42, 4.96, 6.12

D 4.96, 3.42, 2.89, 6.12

16 How many outcomes are there for flipping a coin two times?

F one **H** four

G two **J** eight

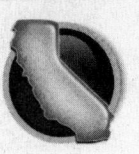

Periodic Assessment 4 (continued)

17 Sharon has a red number cube labeled 1–6. She also has a blue number cube labeled 1–6. There are 36 outcomes for rolling the two number cubes. How many times can you roll a sum of 8?

A 3 out of 36

B 4 out of 36

C 5 out of 36

D 6 out of 36

18 What is the length of the line segment shown on the grid?

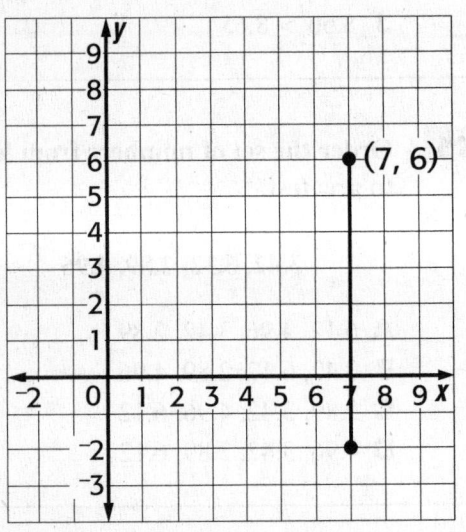

F 2 units

G 6 units

H 7 units

J 8 units

19 Which point is on this line?

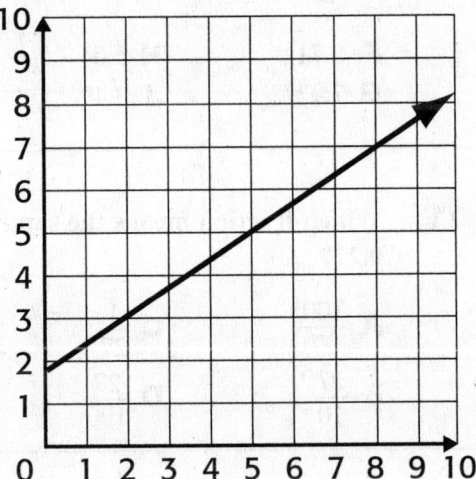

A (2, 4)

B (7, 8)

C (8, 7)

D (8, 5)

20 What is the sum of 6.23 and 3.72?

F 10.95

G 9.95

H 3.51

J 2.51

21 Round 14.57 to the nearest whole number.

A 14

B 14.5

C 14.6

D 15

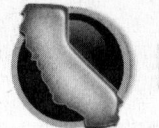

Name _____ Date _____

Periodic Assessment 4 (continued)

22 Brandon has a bag with 5 blue marbles, 3 yellow marbles, and 8 red marbles all the same size. What is the probability that Brandon will draw a red marble?

F $\frac{3}{16}$

G $\frac{5}{16}$

H $\frac{8}{16}$

J $\frac{11}{16}$

23 Which fraction is best represented by point G on this number line?

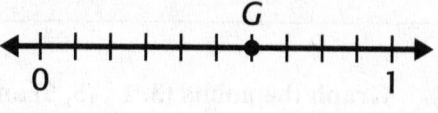
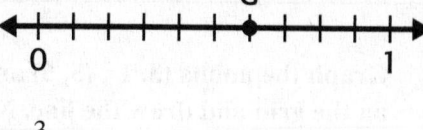

A $\frac{3}{5}$

B $\frac{2}{3}$

C $\frac{7}{10}$

D $\frac{3}{4}$

24 Which of the following has the least value?

F 6.48

G 4.23

H 2.43

J 0.54

25 Look at the line segment shown below.

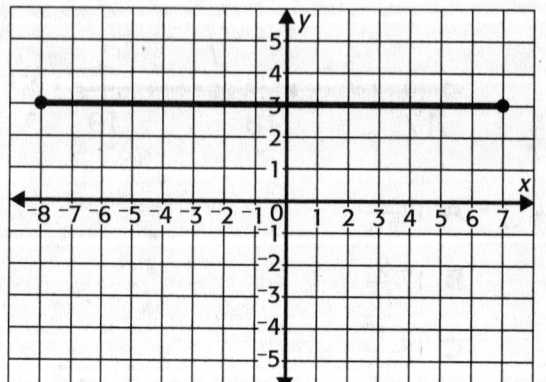

What is the length of the line segment?

A 3 units

B 7 units

C 8 units

D 15 units

26 Point L is at (3, 6) and Point M is at (3, 2). How can you find the length of LM?

F Add 3 and 3

G Add 6 and 2

H Subtract 3 and 3

J Subtract 6 and 2

Periodic Assessment 4 (continued)

27 On the number line below, what number does point *J* represent?

J

17   18   19

A $17\frac{3}{10}$

B $17\frac{9}{10}$

C $18\frac{1}{10}$

D $18\frac{3}{10}$

28 Look at the graph. Point *M* is at (5, 9). Point *N* is at (5, 2).

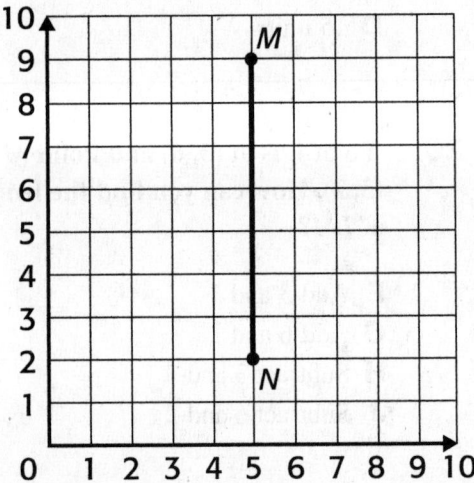

How can you find the number of units from point *M* to point *N*?

F Subtract 9 and 2

G Subtract 5 and 2

H Add 7 and 2

J Add 9 and 2

29 The hospital is 255.68 feet tall. What is the height of the hospital rounded to the nearest whole number?

A 250 feet   **C** 256 feet

B 255 feet   **D** 260 feet

30 Which letter is located at $\frac{1}{3}$ on the number line below?

C   B   A   D

0   1   2   3   4   5   6

F *A*   **H** *C*

G *B*   **J** *D*

31 Graph the points (3, 1), (5, 5) and (7, 9) on the grid and draw the line. Name two more points and explain how you know they are on the line.

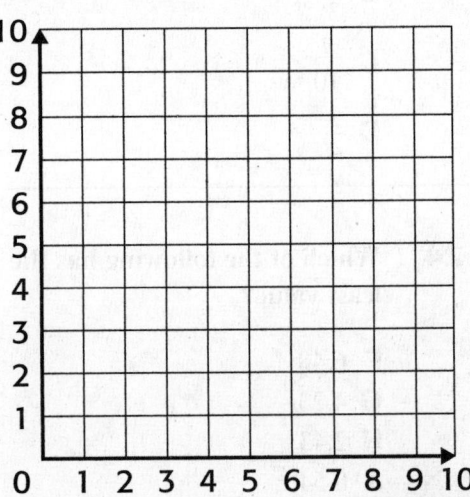

Stop

Periodic Assessment 1
Student Answer Sheet

Record your answers by coloring in the appropriate bubble for the best answer to each question.

1 Ⓐ Ⓑ Ⓒ Ⓓ	11 Ⓐ Ⓑ Ⓒ Ⓓ	21 Ⓐ Ⓑ Ⓒ Ⓓ
2 Ⓕ Ⓖ Ⓗ Ⓙ	12 Ⓕ Ⓖ Ⓗ Ⓙ	22 Ⓕ Ⓖ Ⓗ Ⓙ
3 Ⓐ Ⓑ Ⓒ Ⓓ	13 Ⓐ Ⓑ Ⓒ Ⓓ	23 Ⓐ Ⓑ Ⓒ Ⓓ
4 Ⓕ Ⓖ Ⓗ Ⓙ	14 Ⓕ Ⓖ Ⓗ Ⓙ	24 Ⓕ Ⓖ Ⓗ Ⓙ
5 Ⓐ Ⓑ Ⓒ Ⓓ	15 Ⓐ Ⓑ Ⓒ Ⓓ	25 Ⓐ Ⓑ Ⓒ Ⓓ
6 Ⓕ Ⓖ Ⓗ Ⓙ	16 Ⓕ Ⓖ Ⓗ Ⓙ	26 Ⓕ Ⓖ Ⓗ Ⓙ
7 Ⓐ Ⓑ Ⓒ Ⓓ	17 Ⓐ Ⓑ Ⓒ Ⓓ	27 Ⓐ Ⓑ Ⓒ Ⓓ
8 Ⓕ Ⓖ Ⓗ Ⓙ	18 Ⓕ Ⓖ Ⓗ Ⓙ	28 Ⓕ Ⓖ Ⓗ Ⓙ
9 Ⓐ Ⓑ Ⓒ Ⓓ	19 Ⓐ Ⓑ Ⓒ Ⓓ	29 Ⓐ Ⓑ Ⓒ Ⓓ
10 Ⓕ Ⓖ Ⓗ Ⓙ	20 Ⓕ Ⓖ Ⓗ Ⓙ	30 Ⓕ Ⓖ Ⓗ Ⓙ

Write your answer for Question 31 in the space below. Show all your work or reasoning.

Periodic Assessment 1
Student Answer Sheet

Record your answers by coloring in the appropriate bubble for the best answer to each question.

Write your answer for Question 11 in the space below. Show all your work or reasoning

California Mathematics, Grade 4, Standards Practice 85B

Periodic Assessment 2
Student Answer Sheet

Record your answers by coloring in the appropriate bubble for the best answer to each question.

1 Ⓐ Ⓑ Ⓒ Ⓓ	11 Ⓐ Ⓑ Ⓒ Ⓓ	21 Ⓐ Ⓑ Ⓒ Ⓓ
2 Ⓕ Ⓖ Ⓗ Ⓙ	12 Ⓕ Ⓖ Ⓗ Ⓙ	22 Ⓕ Ⓖ Ⓗ Ⓙ
3 Ⓐ Ⓑ Ⓒ Ⓓ	13 Ⓐ Ⓑ Ⓒ Ⓓ	23 Ⓐ Ⓑ Ⓒ Ⓓ
4 Ⓕ Ⓖ Ⓗ Ⓙ	14 Ⓕ Ⓖ Ⓗ Ⓙ	24 Ⓕ Ⓖ Ⓗ Ⓙ
5 Ⓐ Ⓑ Ⓒ Ⓓ	15 Ⓐ Ⓑ Ⓒ Ⓓ	25 Ⓐ Ⓑ Ⓒ Ⓓ
6 Ⓕ Ⓖ Ⓗ Ⓙ	16 Ⓕ Ⓖ Ⓗ Ⓙ	26 Ⓕ Ⓖ Ⓗ Ⓙ
7 Ⓐ Ⓑ Ⓒ Ⓓ	17 Ⓐ Ⓑ Ⓒ Ⓓ	27 Ⓐ Ⓑ Ⓒ Ⓓ
8 Ⓕ Ⓖ Ⓗ Ⓙ	18 Ⓕ Ⓖ Ⓗ Ⓙ	28 Ⓕ Ⓖ Ⓗ Ⓙ
9 Ⓐ Ⓑ Ⓒ Ⓓ	19 Ⓐ Ⓑ Ⓒ Ⓓ	29 Ⓐ Ⓑ Ⓒ Ⓓ
10 Ⓕ Ⓖ Ⓗ Ⓙ	20 Ⓕ Ⓖ Ⓗ Ⓙ	30 Ⓕ Ⓖ Ⓗ Ⓙ

Write your answer for Question 31 in the space below. Show all your work or reasoning.

Periodic Assessment 2
Student Answer Sheet

Record your answers by coloring in the appropriate bubble for the best answer to each question.

Write your answer for Question 31 in the space below. Show all your work or reasoning.

Name _____ Date _____

 # Periodic Assessment 3
Student Answer Sheet

Record your answers by coloring in the appropriate bubble for the best answer to each question.

1 ⒶⒷⒸⒹ	11 ⒶⒷⒸⒹ	21 ⒶⒷⒸⒹ
2 ⒻⒼⒽⒿ	12 ⒻⒼⒽⒿ	22 ⒻⒼⒽⒿ
3 ⒶⒷⒸⒹ	13 ⒶⒷⒸⒹ	23 ⒶⒷⒸⒹ
4 ⒻⒼⒽⒿ	14 ⒻⒼⒽⒿ	24 ⒻⒼⒽⒿ
5 ⒶⒷⒸⒹ	15 ⒶⒷⒸⒹ	25 ⒶⒷⒸⒹ
6 ⒻⒼⒽⒿ	16 ⒻⒼⒽⒿ	26 ⒻⒼⒽⒿ
7 ⒶⒷⒸⒹ	17 ⒶⒷⒸⒹ	27 ⒶⒷⒸⒹ
8 ⒻⒼⒽⒿ	18 ⒻⒼⒽⒿ	28 ⒻⒼⒽⒿ
9 ⒶⒷⒸⒹ	19 ⒶⒷⒸⒹ	29 ⒶⒷⒸⒹ
10 ⒻⒼⒽⒿ	20 ⒻⒼⒽⒿ	30 ⒻⒼⒽⒿ

Write your answer for Question 31 in the space below. Show all your work or reasoning.

Periodic Assessment 4
Student Answer Sheet

Record your answers by coloring in the appropriate bubble for the best answer to each question.

1 Ⓐ Ⓑ Ⓒ Ⓓ	11 Ⓐ Ⓑ Ⓒ Ⓓ	21 Ⓐ Ⓑ Ⓒ Ⓓ
2 Ⓕ Ⓖ Ⓗ Ⓙ	12 Ⓕ Ⓖ Ⓗ Ⓙ	22 Ⓕ Ⓖ Ⓗ Ⓙ
3 Ⓐ Ⓑ Ⓒ Ⓓ	13 Ⓐ Ⓑ Ⓒ Ⓓ	23 Ⓐ Ⓑ Ⓒ Ⓓ
4 Ⓕ Ⓖ Ⓗ Ⓙ	14 Ⓕ Ⓖ Ⓗ Ⓙ	24 Ⓕ Ⓖ Ⓗ Ⓙ
5 Ⓐ Ⓑ Ⓒ Ⓓ	15 Ⓐ Ⓑ Ⓒ Ⓓ	25 Ⓐ Ⓑ Ⓒ Ⓓ
6 Ⓕ Ⓖ Ⓗ Ⓙ	16 Ⓕ Ⓖ Ⓗ Ⓙ	26 Ⓕ Ⓖ Ⓗ Ⓙ
7 Ⓐ Ⓑ Ⓒ Ⓓ	17 Ⓐ Ⓑ Ⓒ Ⓓ	27 Ⓐ Ⓑ Ⓒ Ⓓ
8 Ⓕ Ⓖ Ⓗ Ⓙ	18 Ⓕ Ⓖ Ⓗ Ⓙ	28 Ⓕ Ⓖ Ⓗ Ⓙ
9 Ⓐ Ⓑ Ⓒ Ⓓ	19 Ⓐ Ⓑ Ⓒ Ⓓ	29 Ⓐ Ⓑ Ⓒ Ⓓ
10 Ⓕ Ⓖ Ⓗ Ⓙ	20 Ⓕ Ⓖ Ⓗ Ⓙ	30 Ⓕ Ⓖ Ⓗ Ⓙ

Write your answer for Question 31 in the space below. Show all your work or reasoning.

Workspace

Workspace